CIRIA C532

Control of water pollution from construction sites
Guidance for consultants and contractors

Hugh Masters-Williams

Andy Heap

Heather Kitts

Lutaf Greenshaw

Steve Davis

Peter Fisher

Martyn Hendrie

Dave Owens

CIRIA *sharing knowledge* ■ *building best practice*

6 Storey's Gate, Westminster, London SW1P 3AU
TELEPHONE 020 7222 8891   FAX 020 7222 1708
EMAIL enquiries@ciria.org.uk
WEBSITE www.ciria.org.uk

Summary

This guidance document provides practical help for consultants and contractors on how to plan and manage construction projects to control water pollution. It has seven main chapters.

1. Benefits and obligations

2. Water pollution from construction

3. Legislative framework

4. Construction contracts

5. Managing water pollution from construction

6. Water management techniques

7. Summary and recommendations

This document is intended as a user-friendly guide, a reference book and a training aid. It reinforces and builds upon the principles relating to the control of water pollution from construction sites developed in previous CIRIA publications.

Control of water pollution from construction sites. Guidance for consultants and contractors

Masters-Williams, H, Heap, A, Kitts, H, Greenshaw, L, Davis, S, Fisher, P, Hendrie, M, Owens, D

Construction Industry Research and Information Association

CIRIA C532   © CIRIA 2001   ISBN 0 86017 532 4

This book also constitutes Environment Agency R&D Technical Report P357

Keywords		
Water quality, surface water, groundwater, construction cycle, contractor, consultant, environmental management, pollution prevention, pollution mitigation		

Reader interest	Classification	
Contractors, consultants (clients, regulators, local planning authorities)	Availability	Unrestricted
	Content	Advice/guidance
	Status	Committee-guided
	Users	Construction professionals and managers

Acknowledgements

This is the project report for CIRIA Research Project 585, "The control of water pollution from construction sites – guidance for consultants and contractors".

The work was carried out by Hyder Consulting with support from COSTAIN Civil Engineering. The principal contributors from Hyder Consulting were Hugh Masters-Williams, Andy Heap, Heather Kitts, Lutaf Greenshaw, Steve Davies and Nicola Martin. From COSTAIN Civil Engineering they were Peter Fisher, Martyn Hendrie and Dave Owens.

Funders

The research leading to the publication of the guidance document was funded by:

- CIRIA Core Programme
- Environment Agency
- Department of the Environment, Transport and the Regions under the Partners in Innovation Programme, Construction Directorate
- The BOC Foundation
- Scottish and Northern Ireland Forum for Environmental Research
- The CAPITB Trust through the European Social Fund (ADAPT Supply chain environmental training project).

Project steering group

CIRIA wish to express its thanks to the members of the project steering group for their contributions to the work:

Peter Hurrell (chairman)	independent construction adviser
Alison Barker	FBE Management
Trevor Higgs	Construction Confederation
Rosanna Joel	Alfred McAlpine
Alastair McNeill	Scottish Environment Protection Agency (SEPA)
George Paschke	Wren and Bell
Marcus Pearson	Balfour Beatty Major Projects
Stan Redfearn	The BOC Foundation
Peter Rudd	Environment Agency.

Thanks also go to the corresponding member of the steering group:

Abdul Thomas	The CAPITB Trust (through the European Social Fund ADAP Supply chain environmental training project).

CIRIA's research manager for this project was Craig Elliott.

CIRIA and the authors gratefully acknowledge the support of these funding organisations and the technical help and advise provided by the members of the steering group. Contributions do not imply that individual funders necessarily endorse all views expressed in published outputs.

In addition to the steering group members, CIRIA is grateful to the following organisations for providing photographs, supporting information and feedback on this study:

- Bovis Europe
- DoE Northern Ireland
- Edmund Nuttall
- Environment and Heritage Service, Northern Ireland
- Environmental Resources Management Limited
- Golder Associates
- Johnston Construction
- Laing
- MacTaggart and Mickel
- Miller Civil Engineering
- Nicholas Pearson Associates
- Ove Arup
- Posford Duvivier
- Power Lines Pipes and Cables
- Raynesway Construction
- Tarmac Building
- The Scottish Office
- Severn Trent
- University of Bath
- Watson Construction
- Weeks
- Welsh Office
- Willis Coroon
- Young Associates.

The target audience

Environmental issues arise throughout a construction project. People working in construction have to be aware of their environmental obligations and the benefits that good practice will bring at every stage from the initial feasibility studies through to design, construction planning and the actual works on site. As the environmental issues differ at each stage, the approach to resolving them may also differ accordingly.

This guidance document provides help on environmental good practice for control of water pollution arising from construction activities. It is intended for use by:

- project promoters
- site managers
- site engineers
- site foremen and site supervisors
- project managers
- contract supervisors/resident engineers.

It is relevant to all organisations represented on a construction site, whether as a promoter, designer, main contractor or a subcontractor.

The consequences of environmental planning, or lack of planning, by people involved in the early stages of a project's development can have a profound effect on the ability of the site staff to meet their obligations. Due to this, other construction professionals should seek to understand the site environmental good practice presented in this guidance document. These include:

- construction planners within contractors' main offices
- contractors
- project managers
- project directors
- designers
- clients
- construction managers
- planning supervisors and principal contractors.

Much of the advice contained in this guidance document is based on practices that have been carried out on construction sites for many years, but many of the ideas are recent. Therefore it is a guidance document for all levels of construction experience, from the young site engineer to the experienced site manager.

How to use this guide

This book has been designed so that it is not necessary to read it from cover to cover to find the required guidance. However, the control of water pollution on construction sites relies on a planned and integrated approach. For readers not familiar with the key issues, limited reading of specific topics within this guidance document may not provide all the necessary information to plan ahead and avoid water pollution. Therefore, it is suggested that a reader new to the concepts of water pollution control should read the complete guidance document before concentrating on the specific methodologies outlined in Section 6. A brief description of the contents of each section is given below.

Section 1 introduces the reader to the importance of taking water quality issues into consideration as part of the construction process.

Section 2 provides the reader with an introduction to the properties of natural water-bodies, types of common pollutant associated with construction sites and their sources, transportation and impact.

Section 3 outlines the legislation that relates to the control of water pollution on site and highlights some key health and safety issues.

Section 4 reviews commonly used construction contracts and outlines their deficiencies and benefits in preventing water pollution.

Section 5 tackles management issues and outlines how good site management can prevent pollution.

Section 6 describes common site activities and identifies how they can result in water pollution. Methods to modify these activities and to treat water pollution on site are also contained within this section.

Section 7 provides conclusions and recommendations arising from "Control of water pollution – guidance for consultants and contractors" (CIRIA Research Project RP585).

Section 8 contains references used within the guidance.

Section 9 contains a list of documents for further reading.

Figures, photographs, case studies and site procedures have been included throughout the document to help illustrate the written text. These are included to demonstrate how good practice may be applied on site and also to illustrate how poor practice can result in pollution incidents and subsequent prosecution.

Good/bad practice is clearly indicated in photographs and case studies by "happy/sad face" icons.

The glossary contains some of the most commonly used terms relating to water quality and related construction site activities.

Coverage of this guide

This guide addresses water quality issues from the inception of a construction project through to the completion of the construction stage and beyond into decommissioning. The book describes the sources and movement of water through a construction site, along with the types of water pollution typically associated with site activities. It defines the chemical properties of natural waterbodies and commonly encountered indicators of water pollution. It looks at the way in which environment regulators categorise the severity of pollution incidents and details the legislative framework controlling water quality. It also describes the associated health and safety issues.

In using this report you should be clear about the limits of the scope of the guidance provided. In particular:

- it is not a health and safety manual
- it should not replace contact with regulators
- although it gives an overview of legislation, detailed guidance should be sought from the company's environmental representative (or external specialists) or legal advisers
- in all instances, when dealing with the issues covered do not take action beyond your expertise. If in doubt, seek specialist advice.

The guide is generally relevant for all types of contract conditions – traditional, design-and-build, design–build–finance–operate (DBFO) and partnering. With some types of contract the contractor carries the risk of cost or programme delays caused by unexpected events or occurrences relating to water quality issues. It is the contractor's responsibility to be aware of the relevant issues and to manage the site effectively to avoid damage to the aquatic environment. If in doubt, seek guidance from your company's environmental representative, an environmental consultant or environment regulator.

Regional differences in legislation

This book provides guidance to consultants and contractors on the control of water pollution from construction sites. It sets out generic good practice and procedures for controlling water pollution on construction sites in the United Kingdom. The generic good practice and procedures are generally appropriate for use in England, Wales, Scotland and Northern Ireland. The reader should note that there are regional legislative or regulatory variations; attention is drawn to some of the most relevant of these in the text. However, anyone intending to implement the good practices and procedures set out in this book should ensure that the work complies with these regional variations in legislation. The local regulator will be able to advise on these matters.

Any reference to the environment regulator should be read to include:

- Environment Agency (with jurisdiction over England and Wales)
- Scottish Environment Protection Agency (SEPA)
- Northern Ireland Environment and Heritage Service
- Department of Public Services in Jersey and Guernsey.

At the time of printing the main telephone numbers for the environment regulators are:

Environment Agency, Head Office, Bristol	01454 624 400
SEPA, Head Office, Stirling	01786 457 700
Environment and Heritage Service, Environmental Protection, Belfast	01232 254 754

Further information, including published documents, can be obtained from the websites of the above organisations:

England	www.environment-agency.gov.uk
Wales	www.environment-agency.wales.gov.uk
Scotland	www.sepa.org.uk
Northern Ireland	www.ersni.gov.uk

Relationship to other CIRIA guidance

CIRIA has produced three key publications that establish the environmental issues to be addressed at all stages of construction:

- *Environmental good practice on site* (C502, 1999, ISBN 0 86017 502 2), with an associated poster, *Our environment matters* (C502P) and companion pocket book, *Environmental good practice – working on site* (C503, 1999, ISBN 0 86017 503 0).

- *A client's guide to greener construction* (SP120, 1995, ISBN 0 86017 423 9).

- *Environmental handbook for building and civil and engineering projects.*
  Part 1, Design and specification (C512, 2000, ISBN 0 86017 512 X)
  Part 2, Construction phase (C528, 2000, ISBN 0 86017 528 6)
  Part 3, Demolition and site clearance (C529, 2000, ISBN 0 86017 529 4).
  Together, the three volumes constitute an updated and expanded version of CIRIA publications SP97 and SP98 (both published in 1994 and no longer available).

These key publications outline the issues, principles and legislation that should be adopted to improve environmental performance in the construction industry. We list below other CIRIA publications of particular relevance:

- *Building a cleaner future* (SP141V, 1996). A joint CIRIA and Environment Agency pack that includes a training video, booklet and poster

- *Waste minimisation and recycling in construction – a review* (SP122, 1995, ISBN 0 86017 428 X)

- *Waste minimisation in construction – site guide* (SP133, 1997d, ISBN 0 86017 482 4). This outlines current good practice in site waste management and contains information on reducing wastage of raw materials, and reusing and recycling waste materials

- This publication is also contained within *Waste minimisation and recycling in construction – training pack* (SP148, 1998, ISBN 0 86017 488 3), which also includes a video, overheads and disk copies of the pack's documents

- *The Observational Method in ground engineering – principles and applications* (R185, 1999, ISBN 0 86017 497 2). This is specifically relevant to minimising waste in ground engineering and to optimising design to foresee problems on site

- *Managing materials and components on site* (SP146, 1998, ISBN 0 86017 481 6). This is a CIRIA site guide that provides practical guidance for site managers, site engineers and supervisors on how to manage materials and components effectively

- *Sustainable urban drainage systems – design manual for Scotland and Northern Ireland* (C521, 2000, ISBN 0 86017 521 9)

- *Sustainable urban drainage systems – design manual for England and Wales* (C522, 2000, ISBN 0 86017 522 7)

- *Sewerage system management – scoping study* (PR67, 1998, ISBN 0 86017 867 6). This report outlines the issues that need to be addressed to achieve efficient and effective management of sewerage systems

- *Environmental issues in construction – a desk study* (PR73, 1999, ISBN 0 86017 873 0). This report reviews published research and the response of the construction industry to environmental issues

- CIRIA also produced a comprehensive 12-volume reference set on *Remedial treatment for contaminated land* (SP101–112):

  Volume I Introduction and guide (SP101, 1998, ISBN 0 86017 396 8)

  Volume II Decommissioning, decontamination and demolition (SP102, 1995, ISBN 0 86017 397 6)

  Volume III Site investigation and assessment (SP103, 1995, ISBN 0 86017 398 4)

  Volume IV Classification and selection of remedial methods (SP104, 1995, ISBN 0 86017 399 2)

  Volume V Excavation and disposal (SP105, 1995, ISBN 0 86017 400 X)

  Volume VI Containment and hydraulic measures (SP106, 1996, ISBN 0 86017 401 8)

  Volume VII Ex-situ remedial methods for soils, sludges and sediments (SP107, 1995, ISBN 0 86017 402 6)

  Volume VIII Ex-situ remedial methods for contaminated groundwater and other liquids (SP108, 1995, ISBN 0 86017 403 4)

  Volume IX In-situ methods of remediation (SP109, 1995, ISBN 0 86017 404 2)

  Volume X Special situations (SP110, 1995, ISBN 0 86017 405 0)

  Volume XI Planning and management (SP111, 1995, ISBN 0 86017 406 9)

  Volume XII Policy and legislation (SP112, 1998, ISBN 0 86017 407 7).

Further details on the above and other CIRIA publications can be obtained from:
6 Storey's Gate, Westminster, London SW1P 3AU; Tel: 020 7222 8891; fax: 020 7222 1708; email: enquiries@ciria.org.uk; or visit the CIRIA website at www.ciria.org.uk.

Contents

List of figures

List of tables

List of case studies

List of site procedures

The following site procedures relate to preventing water pollution on a major road scheme that crosses several watercourses and Sites of Special Scientific Interest (SSSIs). These are examples only, and any site procedures drawn up should take into account the local environment and constraints required by the environment regulator. These procedures would not replace any standard site procedures relating to health and safety or operating equipment.

Site procedures should be considered "controlled documents" and should be distributed to identified people and locations. They should not be copied indiscriminately. The benefit of tight control is that, when a procedure is changed, the location of all earlier copies is known and they can be withdrawn from circulation before the new procedure is issued. This should prevent staff from working with obsolete versions of site procedures.

All site procedures should be numbered and dated (for example Site Procedure 1 Issued 01/01/2000) and all revisions to them should be numbered and dated (for example SP1 Revision A 01/06/2000). The procedure should identify the contractor responsible for the site and the name of the site to which it relates. Site procedures should also be given authority by containing the signature of the person responsible for the site activities, for example the project manager. Most importantly, lack of compliance with procedures should be seen as a serious breach of site security, and appropriate disciplinary action should be taken to prevent it recurring.

Glossary

Abstraction licence	Licence from a competent authority to remove a fixed volume of water from natural waterbody (surface and groundwater).
Algae	Simple plants ranging from single cells to large plants.
Ammonia	A water-soluble chemical compound, produced by the decomposition of organic material. Ammonia affects the quality of fisheries and the suitability of abstractions for potable water supply. Used as a water quality indicator. Ammonia is a List II substance (see below).
Aquifer	A sub-surface zone or formation of rock or soil containing a body of groundwater.
Archaeology	The study of historic remains, often by excavation.
Benthic	Pertaining to the bed of a river or other body of water.
Bentonite	A colloidal clay, largely made up of the mineral sodium montmorillonite, a hydrated aluminium silicate.
Biodegradable	Capable of being decomposed by bacteria or other living organisms.
BOD	Biochemical oxygen demand is the measure of the concentration of biodegradable organic carbon compounds in solution. Used as a water quality indicator.
Brownfield site	A site that has been previously developed.
Bund	A barrier, dam or mound usually formed from earthworks material and used to contain or exclude water (or other liquids) from an area of the site.
Caisson	A cylindrical or rectangular ring wall usually formed from pre-cast concrete segments and used for excluding water or supporting soft ground in deep excavations.
Casing	An impervious, durable pipe placed in a borehole to prevent the walls of the borehole from collapsing, and to seal off surface drainage or undesirable water, gas or other fluids, and prevent their entrance into such an excavation.
CDM	Construction (Design and Management) Regulations (1994), which emphasise the importance of addressing health and safety issues at the design phase of a construction project.
COD	Chemical oxygen demand is the measure of the amount of oxygen taken up by chemical oxidation of a substance in solution. Used as a water quality indicator.
Cofferdam	A temporary dam, usually of sheet piling driven into the ground to exclude water and provide access to an area that is otherwise submerged or waterlogged.
Cone of depression	A depression in the groundwater table shaped like an inverted cone that develops around a well from which water is being withdrawn.

Construction cycle	The sequence of events or activities carried out in the development of a construction project.
Contaminated ground	Ground that has the presence of such substances which, when present in sufficient quantities or concentrations, are likely to have detri-mental effects on potential targets.
Controlled waters	Almost all natural waters in the UK are controlled waters. They include rivers, streams, ditches, ponds and groundwater. The Environment Agencies are charged with responsibility for policing controlled waters. The Environment Act 1995 defines the term.
Cyprinid fishery	Waters in which coarse fish (those belonging to the Cyprinidae, or other species such as pike, perch and eel) are found.
Detention pond/tank	A pond or tank that has a lower outflow than inflow. Often used to prevent flooding.
Dewatering	The removal of groundwater/surface water to lower the water table.
Diffuse pollution	Pollution that does not rise from an easily identifiable source (such as an effluent discharge pipe). Usually refers to runoff or leaching from land.
Discharge area	An area in which there are upward components of hydraulic head in the aquifer. Groundwater flows towards the surface in a discharge area and may escape as a spring, seep or baseflow, or by evaporation and transpiration.
Discharge consent	Permission to discharge effluent, subject to conditions laid down in the consent, issued by the relevant environment regulator.
Dissolved oxygen (DO)	The amount of oxygen dissolved in water. Oxygen is vital for aquatic life, so this measurement is a test of the health of a river. Used as a water quality indicator.
Drawdown	The distance between the static water level and the surface of lowered water level.
Drainage well	A well used to drain excess water into an aquifer.
Dust	Airborne solid matter up to about 2 mm in size.
Duty of care	The implication of the duty of care is that toxic materials are monitored and administered by an appropriate system each time they pass from one individual to another, or from one process to another. Important information regarding the nature of the material and any appropriate emergency action should also be passed on.
Ecology	All living things, such as trees, flowering plants, insects, birds and mammals, and the habitats in which they live.
Ecosystem	A biological community of interacting organisms and their physical environment.
Environment	Both the natural environment (air, land, water resources, plant and animal life), and the habitats in which they live.

Environment regulators	These include the Environment Agency (in England and Wales), the Scottish Environment Protection Agency, the Environment and Heritage Service in Northern Ireland, and the Department of Public Services in Jersey and Guernsey.
Estuary	A semi-enclosed body of water in which seawater is substantially diluted with freshwater entering from land drainage.
Eutrophication	Enrichment of water by nutrients, especially compounds of nitrogen and/or phosphorus, causing accelerated growth of algae and higher forms of plant life to produce undesirable disturbance to the balance of organisms present in the water and to the quality of the water concerned.
Fauna	The animals found in a particular physical environment.
Filter strip	Vegetated area of land used to accept surface runoff as sheet flow from an upstream area.
Flora	The plants found in a particular physical environment
Grip	A small channel cut into the ground on the uphill side of an excavation to lead rainwater clear of it.
Groundwater	The water in the ground.
Grout	A fluid mixture of cement and water of such a consistency that it can be forced through a pipe and placed as required. Various additives, such as sand, bentonite and hydrated lime, may be included in the mixture to meet certain requirements.
Grouting	The operation by which grout is placed.
Gully erosion	The erosion of soils by surface runoff, resulting typically in steep-sided channels and small ravines, poorly consolidated superficial material or bedrock by streams or runoff water.
Hazard	A property, situation or substance with potential to cause harm.
Heavy metal	Loosely, metals with a high atomic mass (sometimes given as metals with an atomic mass greater than that of calcium; Manahan, 1990), often used in discussion of metal toxicity. No definitive list of heavy metals exists, but they generally include cadmium, zinc, mercury, chromium, lead, nickel, thallium, silver. Some metalloids, eg arsenic and antimony, are classified as heavy metals for discussion of their toxicity.
Heritage bodies	These have a general duty to conserve our heritage, to carry out scheduling of historic remains, and to undertake research. They comprise English Heritage, CADW, Historic Scotland, and the Northern Ireland Environment and Heritage Service.
Invertebrates	Animals that lack a vertebral column. This includes many groups of animals used for biological grading, such as insects, crustaceans, worms and molluscs.
Leaching	The process during which soluble minerals may be removed from the soil by water percolating through it.
Leakage	The flow of water from one hydrologic unit to another. The leakage may be natural, as through a semi-impervious confining layer, or manmade, as through an uncased well.

List I substance	A controlled substance as defined under the Groundwater Regulations 1998 and the Dangerous Substances Directive (76/464/EEC). List I substances are considered the most dangerous in terms of toxicity, bioaccumulation and persistence. These controls *prevent* their discharge to the environment. See Section 3.2.2 for list of substances.
List II substance	A controlled substance as defined under the Groundwater Regulations 1998 and the Dangerous Substances Directive (76/464/EEC). They are less toxic than List I substances but are still capable of harm, hence their discharge to the environment is *limited*. See Section 3.2.2 for list of substances.
Macroinvertebrates	Invertebrate animals of sufficient size to be easily visible to the unaided eye and to be retained in a net with a 1 mm mesh.
Macrophyte	Plants easily visible to the unaided eye.
Metalloid	An element with chemical properties that are intermediate between metals and non-metals. They include: boron, silicon, germanium, arsenic, antimony and tellurium. Although not a metal, arsenic is often included in the term "heavy metal" when its toxicity is being discussed.
Mineral solids	Particles transported in water or air that are from entirely mineral (non-organic) origins.
Nature conservation bodies	The four organisations that have regional responsibility for promoting the conservation of wildlife and natural features: Countryside Council for Wales, English Nature, Northern Ireland Environment and Heritage Service, and Scottish Natural Heritage.
Noise	Often defined as a sound that is not desired. Sound is a wave motion carried by air molecules between the source and the receiver, usually the ear.
Nutrient	A substance providing nourishment for living organisms (such as nitrogen and phosphorus).
Organic pollution	A general term describing the type of pollution that, through the action of bacteria, consumes the dissolved oxygen in rivers. The effects of organic pollution are described by the levels of bio-chemical oxygen demand, ammonia and dissolved oxygen found in a waterbody.
Out-turn value	The final or net value.
Pathway	The route by which potential contaminants may reach targets.
Permeability	The property or capacity of a rock, sediment or soil for transmitting a fluid
Point source pollution	Pollution that arises from an easily identifiable source, usually an effluent discharge pipe.
Pollution	The introduction of a substance that has the potential to cause harm to the environment. Pollutants include silty water, oils, chemicals, litter and mud.
Recharge	The addition of water to the groundwater system by natural or artificial processes.

Recycling	Collecting and separating materials from waste and processing them to produce marketable products.
Redds	Shallow pits excavated by fish in gravel, in which they lay their eggs.
Reduction	Waste reduction has two components: reducing the amount of waste produced, and reducing the hazard of the waste produced.
Reed bed	Area of grass-like marsh plants, primarily adjacent to freshwater. Artificially constructed reed beds can be used to accumulate suspended particles and associated heavy metals, or to treat small quantities of partially treated sewage effluent.
Reuse	Putting objects back into use, without processing, so that they do not remain in the waste stream.
Risk	The chance of an adverse event. The impact of a risk is the combination of the probability of that potential hazard being realised, the severity of the outcome if it is, and the numbers of people exposed to the hazard.
Risk assessment	"A carefully considered judgement" requiring an evaluation of the risk that may arise from the hazards identified, combining the various factors contributing to the risk and then evaluating their significance.
Risk control	The definition of the measures necessary to control the risk, coupled with their implementation; the management of the risk. The risk management process must include the arrangements for monitoring the effectiveness of the control measures together with their review to ensure continuing relevance.
River Habitat Survey	Assessment of the physical qualities of a watercourse that notes any artificial modifications.
Runoff	That part of surface water or precipitation flowing on the ground surface.
Salmonid fishery	Waters in which game fish (such as salmon, trout, grayling and whitefish) are found.
Sedimentation tank/pond	Sedimentation (sometimes called settlement) is a property of a pond or tank – see also **storage pond**, **detention pond** and **stilling pond**.
Sediments	Sediments are the layers of particles that cover the bottom of water-bodies such as lakes, ponds, rivers and reservoirs.
Silt	The generic term for waterborne particles with a grain size of 4–63 μm, ie between clay and sand.
Site of Special Scientific Interest (SSSI)	An area of land or water notified under the Wildlife and Countryside Act 1981 (as amended) as being of geological or nature conservation importance, in the opinion of Countryside Council for Wales, English Nature or Scottish Natural Heritage.
Soil	The terrestrial medium on which many organisms depend, which is a mixture of minerals (produced by chemical, physical and biological weathering of rocks), organic matter and water. It often has high populations of bacteria, fungi and animals such as earthworms.

Special Area of Conservation (SAC)	Established under the EC Habitats Directive (92/43/EEC), implemented in the UK by The Conservation (Natural Habitats etc) Regulations 1994, and The Conservation (Natural Habitats etc) (Northern Ireland) Regulations 1995. The sites are significant in habitat type and species, and are considered in greatest need of conservation at a European Level. All UK SACs are based on SSSIs, but may cover several separate but related sites.
Stilling pond/tank	A pond or tank used to reduce turbulence. The inflow and outflow are equal. Reduced velocity may be required to prevent scouring.
Storage pond/tank	Pond (sometimes called a lagoon) or tank used to hold water, with no outflow.
Sump	A pit that may be lined or unlined and is used to collect water and sediments before being pumped out.
Surface water	Water that appears on the land surface, ie lakes, rivers, streams, standing water, ponds.
Suspended particulate matter (SPM)	Defined as matter (organic and inorganic) in suspension in a natural waterbody which is smaller than 63 μm and which will not pass through a filter of pore size of 0.45 μm.
Suspended solids	General term describing suspended material. Used as a water quality indicator. See also **suspended particulate matter**.
Swale	An open grassed drainage channel in which surface water may be stored or conveyed that can remove some pollutants.
Target (receptor)	An entity (human, animal, water, vegetation or building) vulnerable to the potential adverse effects of a hazard.
Unconfined aquifer	An aquifer where the water table is exposed to the atmosphere through openings in the overlying materials.
Waste	Any substance or object that the holder discards, intends to discard, or is required to discard.
Wastewater treatment works (WWTW)	Installation to treat and make less toxic domestic and/or industrial effluent.
Watercourse	A natural or artificial linear structure that transports water (rivers, canals, culverts etc).
Water table	The point where the surface of groundwater can be detected. The water table may change with the seasons and the annual rainfall.
Well	Any excavation that is drilled, cored, bored, washed, fractured, driven, dug, jetted, or otherwise constructed when the intended use is for the location, monitoring, dewatering, observation, diversion, artificial recharge, or acquisition of groundwater, or for conducting a pumping aquifer test.
Wetland	Flooded area in which the water is shallow enough to enable the growth of bottom-rooted plants.
Wetted perimeter	The length of the line of contact between the liquid and the channel boundary at that section.

Abbreviations

ACOP	approved code of practice
AOD	above ordnance datum
BOD	biochemical oxygen demand
BS	British Standard
CCW	Countryside Council for Wales
CDM	Construction (Design and Management) Regulations (1994)
CEFAS	Centre for Environment, Fisheries and Aquaculture Science
CICS	common incident classification system
CIRIA	Construction Industry Research and Information Association
CLR	Contaminated Land Research
COD	chemical oxygen demand
COMA	Control of Major Accident Regulations (1999)
COPA 1974	Control of Pollution Act 1974
COPR	Control of Pesticides Regulations (1986)
COSHH	Control of Substances Hazardous to Health (1988)
CPO	county planning officers
DARD	Department of Agriculture and Rural Development (Northern Ireland)
DBFO	design–build–finance–operate
DC	direct current
DETR	Department of the Environment, Transport and the Regions
DO	dissolved oxygen
DoE (NI)	Department of Environment (Northern Ireland)
EA 1995	Environment Act 1995
ECC	*Engineering and construction contract* 2nd edition (ICE, 1995)
ECS	*Engineering and construction subcontract*
EHS	Environment and Heritage Service (Northern Ireland)
ELO	environment liaison officer
EMS	environment management system
EPA 1990	Environmental Protection Act 1990
FCB	Fisheries Conservancy Board (Northern Ireland)
FEPA 1985	Food and Environment Protection Act 1985
GL	ground level
GQA	general quality assessment

GRP	glass-reinforced plastic
HMIP	Her Majesty's Inspectorate of Pollution (superseded by Environment Agency)
HMS	habitat modification score
HQA	habitat quality assessment
HSC	Health and Safety Commission
IDB	Internal Drainage Board
ICE	Institution of Civil Engineers
IchemE	Institution of Chemical Engineers
ISO	International Standards Organisation
JCT	Joint Contracts Tribunal
LA	local authority
MAFF	Ministry of Agriculture, Fisheries and Food (superseded by CEFAS)
MEL	maximum exposure limit
MSDS	manufacturer's safety data sheet
NRA	National Rivers Authority (superseded by Environment Agency)
NTU	nephelometric turbidity unit
OCP	OFTEC (see below) *Code of practice*
OES	Occupational Exposure Standard
OFTEC	Oil Firing Technical Association for the Petroleum Industry
PPG	Pollution Prevention Guideline
RHS	River Habitat Survey
SAC	Special Area of Conservation
SEPA	Scottish Environment Protection Agency
SPM	suspended particulate matter
SSSI	Site of Special Scientific Interest
SUDS	sustainable urban drainage system
TRRL	Transport and Road Research Laboratory
WA 1989	Water Act 1989
WA(NI) 1972	Water Act (Northern Ireland) 1972
WIA 1991	Water Industry Act 1991
WL	water level
WRA	Water Resources Act 1991 (England and Wales)
WWTW	wastewater treatment works
μm	micron (ie 1×10^{-6} m)
μS	microsiemens (unit of conductivity)

1 Benefits and obligations

1.1 ENVIRONMENTAL AND ECONOMIC BENEFITS

Construction sites have historically contributed significantly to the damage of the aquatic environment. This has resulted largely from fuel oil spills and releases of suspended solids to watercourses. Such uncontrolled activities have caused, for example, the contamination of potable water supplies, kills of fish and invertebrates, obliteration of benthic and bank-side habitats and aesthetic degradation. This book focuses on the potential sources of water pollution from within construction sites and effective methods of preventing its occurrence.

Given current awareness of environmental matters, efforts are being made at all levels within the construction industry to implement general environmental improvements:

1. The boards of construction companies are demonstrating their commitment by preparing environmental policies, and in some cases by introducing environmental management systems, some of which comply with the recognised standards of ISO 14001.
2. Clients are requesting evidence of environmental credentials from contractors before awarding contracts.
3. Various environmental initiatives are already being implemented on site.

However, directed action is still needed to improve the performance of the construction industry with respect to protecting the quality of natural waterbodies (surface water and groundwater). Within the industrial sector, construction contributes the largest number of pollution incidents (Section 2.6, Figure 2.4 and Figure 2.5).

There are two major incentives for improving performance:

*   environmental benefits – protected and enhanced water quality and river habitats resulting from good practice
*   economic benefits – avoidance of fines for water pollution incidents and fees for clean-up activities, and lower expenditure on water resources and discharge fees through reduced water usage.

1.1.1 Environmental benefits

More effective water management produces the following benefits:

*   reduced damage to the aquatic environment – uncontrolled construction activities can severely degrade natural waterbodies and their associated flora and fauna. Both the design and the site teams are responsible for ensuring that they take all reasonable steps to prevent damage. Directly or indirectly, a well-designed and managed site can even help to improve water quality
*   reduced demand for water resources – in some areas of the UK and at certain times of the year, water availability is limited. Some predictions suggest that this situation is likely to worsen. Minimising the use of water on site and recycling water on site where possible will reduce the site's total demand over its lifetime

* reduced degradation of potable supplies – contamination of groundwaters and surface waters used as potable supplies can result in high treatment costs or, in some circumstances, preclude them from being used, temporarily or permanently

* reduced concern of local residents – changes in the aesthetic quality of a waterbody raise concerns from local residents and recreational users. By complaining or taking legal action, local residents may delay a project and increase costs. By informing people of temporary changes in flows or quality resulting from essential activities, disruption to work should be minimised.

1.1.2   Economic benefits

The economic benefits of good water management are undeniably important. Implementation does not need to be costly and sound environmental practice makes good economic sense. The economic benefits resulting from implementation can include, but are not limited to:

* improved opportunities to tender – clients in the UK and the rest of Europe are increasingly choosing contractors that can demonstrate good water quality management. A record of prosecutions will damage a contractor's chances of being invited to tender

* less money wasted on fines – fines for water pollution are increasing, but when legal fees and management time are taken into account, the real cost of a prosecution can be 20 times the amount of the fine levied

* less time and money spent repairing environmental damage – all spillages need to be cleaned up and polluted rivers may need to be restocked with fish. Cleaning polluted groundwater is also very expensive. In many cases clean-up can delay the project's progress and permission to resume construction work will not normally be given until remediation has been completed

* less money lost through wasted water resources – controlled and considered use of clean water on site can reduce purchasing and transportation costs and can minimise fees and environmental problems associated with disposal of contaminated water

* improved environmental performance will result in an improved environmental profile – this will help to establish good relationships with environment regulators and local authorities, helping to ensure that projects run smoothly. It will also assist in developing staff morale and make it easier to recruit and retain good staff.

1.2   ENVIRONMENTAL OBLIGATIONS

In addition to the benefits gained from effective water management, the following legislative and contractual controls demand that good practice be followed:

* *national legislation* – in place to protect both the natural environment and construction sites' neighbours. The Environment Agency in England and Wales, and the Scottish Environment Protection Agency (SEPA) in Scotland, polices legislation such as the Environment Act 1995, the Environmental Protection Act 1990 (UK), the Water Resources Act 1991 (England and Wales) and the Control of Pollution Act 1974 (Scotland). In Northern Ireland the legislative framework is different, and water pollution comes under the Water Act (Northern Ireland) 1972 with subsequent amendments. The Act is enforced by the Environment and Heritage Service of the Department of Environment (Northern Ireland). Other legislation is in place to protect specific features of the environment.

    Under such legislation, sites may be designated and protected by virtue of their ecological, archaeological, geological or geomorphological interest. The legislative framework in the UK is discussed in greater detail in Section 3

- *local control* – under the powers given to them by national legislation, local planning authorities or drainage boards may impose requirements on the control of construction site activities adjacent to waterbodies

- *specification and contract conditions* – these will have been drawn up to address any conditions imposed on the contract through the planning system as well as any commitments made by the developer to the local communities. They may also include provisions made in an environmental assessment for the project. Failure to comply will be penalised through the contract

- *corporate control* – many companies have corporate environmental policies and some may require sites to follow environmental management systems. In addition, there may be a specific environmental plan for a particular project. Most major construction companies have an environmental policy that requires the site to adopt controls to minimise environmental damage.

2 Water pollution from construction

2.1 INTRODUCTION

This section describes the sources of water likely to be encountered on construction sites and their properties, the various pollutants arising on construction sites and the pathways by which pollutants can enter controlled waters. It includes a review of the system used by the environment regulators for categorising incidents and a description of the indicators of pollution.

Materials used or generated on construction sites or in construction activities can contaminate surface waters. Pollutants commonly include suspended solids, oil, chemicals, cement, cleaning materials and paints. Contaminated surface waters can be discharged directly into controlled waters or via surface water or foul water drains. These discharges can seriously affect the quality of the receiving waters.

The absence of a visible waterway near the construction site should not preclude concern over water pollution. Dry ditches become natural drainage channels after rainfall and are thus an integral component of a watercourse system. Old underground field drains may be present and probably link directly to controlled waters. Pollutants seeping through the ground can cause serious harm to groundwater or streams, which can affect, for example, abstracted water supplies. Below-ground operations such as piling or tunnelling can open up vertical or horizontal pathways for pollutant or leachate migration into underlying aquifers. Furthermore, the site itself may be contaminated, in which case physical disturbance of the ground has the potential to mobilise contaminants, ultimately leading to pollution of controlled waters.

Aquatic pollution from construction sites may be both long-term, as in the case of dewatering a major site, and short-term, such as an accidental oil spillage.

2.2 SOURCES OF WATER ON CONSTRUCTION SITES

In planning to prevent and minimise water pollution on construction sites, it is important to establish the sources of water likely to be encountered before starting work on the site. Correct identification of the source and its significance will enable you to avoid pollution. For the purposes of this book, four sources have been identified: rainwater, surface water, groundwater and mains/tankered water. Assessment of the quality of these water sources has been included, where appropriate.

2.2.1 Rainwater

Rainfall across the UK varies geographically, seasonally and annually (see Figure 2.1). The weather is dominated by low-pressure systems, which approach from the Atlantic, producing higher rainfall in the west of the UK (Northern Ireland, Wales, south-west England and west Scotland). Winter months are generally wetter than summer months and there can be considerable annual variations with unpredictable high and low rainfall years. In some regions, this can result either in summer droughts or in serious flooding.

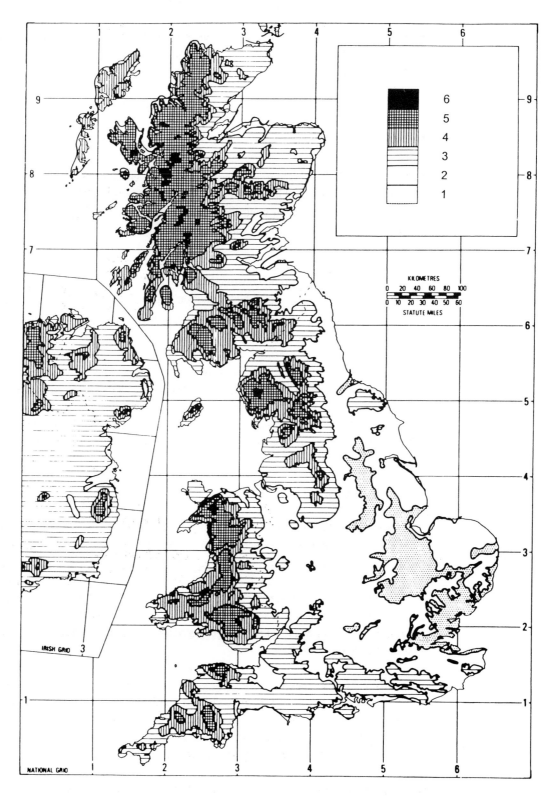

Region	Standard annual average rainfall (mm)	Rainfall depth (mm) 10-year return period	
		24-hour duration	Eight-day duration
1	< 600	29	54
2	600–800	32	65
3	800–1200	41	95
4	1200–1600	52	120
5	1600–3200	88	231
6	> 3200	106	288

Figure 2.1 *Average annual rainfall for the UK (source: PPG2,* Above-ground oil storage tanks*)*

Rainfall can have a significant impact on the pollution of watercourses, as heavy rain and flooding can transport construction site materials that under dry weather conditions would pose no risk to water quality. Consideration therefore needs to be given to the appropriate storage of materials in wet weather. Certain site activities may need to be postponed during rainfall to prevent pollution entering watercourses.

Climate-change predictions suggest that the geographical variation in rainfall will increase, with higher total annual rain in the west and drier summers in the east. This may mean that greater attention will have to be paid to managing site runoff and better use made of accurate weather forecasting in planning site activities.

2.2.2   Surface water

Surface waters include watercourses (rivers, streams, drainage channels, canals) and waterbodies (lakes and reservoirs). Their uses include potable supply, general amenity, boating, swimming, tow/footpaths, conservation, fisheries, industrial abstraction and aesthetic value. Surface waters may be within, or adjacent to, the construction site and their quality must be maintained throughout the construction process.

The quality of surface waters is assessed by the Environment Agency, EHS and SEPA, using comparable systems. These systems enable the environment regulators to identify sources of pollution and to monitor temporal and spatial changes in quality. This information is then used in the agencies' policy decisions to control and license activities that affect water quality. The following is an overview of the assessment systems used by the environment regulators.

England, Wales and Northern Ireland

The Environment Agency and the EHS determine the quality of rivers and canals in England, Wales and Northern Ireland, respectively. Both organisations use the chemical and biological General Quality Assessment (GQA) schemes, which have six classes describing the characteristics and likely uses of a section of river (see Table 2.1). Note that one river may have different classes assigned to defined stretches within it. In England and Wales, approximately 40 000 km of rivers are classified under the chemical scheme and 37 000 km under the biological scheme. More than 2000 km of river are classified in Northern Ireland.

The chemical GQA classifications are based on the concentrations of biochemical oxygen demand (BOD) and ammonia, which are indicators of organic pollution, and dissolved oxygen (DO), which can be affected by the presence of these and other pollutants (see Section 2.3). Sites for the chemical GQA are sampled at least 12 times a year and data collected over a three-year period is used for the assessment.

The biological GQA is based on macro-invertebrate communities, including insect larvae, snails, worms and many other groups of animals found living in the river bed (Environment Agency, 1997). Samples for the biological assessment are collected twice a year, in spring and autumn, from each site. The biological GQA has the advantage that the organisms are continuously exposed to the water quality and are therefore affected by pollution incidents that may not be picked up by the intermittent water quality sampling for the chemical GQA.

It is the remit of both the Environment Agency and EHS to ensure that water quality classes are maintained and improved upon wherever possible. Hence, the governing criterion for consent to discharge is that it will not cause deterioration in the class of the receiving watercourse.

Table 2.1   *GQA classification system (England, Wales and Northern Ireland) (source: EHS, 1995)*

GQA	General description	Likely uses and characteristics [a]
A	Very good	• All abstractions • Very good salmonid fisheries • Cyprinid fisheries • Natural ecosystem
B	Good	• All abstractions • Salmonid fisheries • Cyprinid fisheries • Ecosystem at or close to natural
C	Fairly good	• Potable supply after advanced treatment • Other abstractions • Good cyprinid fisheries • A natural ecosystem, or one corresponding to a good cyprinid fishery
D	Fair	• Potable supply after advanced treatment • Other abstractions • Fair cyprinid fisheries • Impacted ecosystem
E	Poor	• Low-grade abstraction for industry • Fish absent, sporadically present, vulnerable to pollution [b] • Impoverished ecosystem [b]
F	Bad	• Very polluted rivers which may cause nuisance • Severely restricted ecosystem

[a] Provided other standards are met.

[b] Where the class is caused by discharges of organic pollution.

Scotland

SEPA classifies more than 50 000 km of rivers. The water quality classification scheme assesses chemical, biological, nutrient and aesthetic status. Chemical components include indicators of organic, toxic and nutrient pollution (dissolved oxygen, BOD, total reactive phosphorus, ammonia, pH, iron and dangerous substances). Biological assessment is based on invertebrates and aesthetic quality is based on litter. The river classes are: excellent, good, fair, poor and seriously polluted.

Lochs form a significant proportion of the water within Scotland, with approximately 27 000 being identified on maps at a scale of 1:50 000. SEPA classifies the 150 lochs with a surface area above 1 km^2 and 23 smaller lochs (SEPA, 1999). They are classified on a five-year cycle, with the next national survey planned for 2000. Classication is based on chemical measures to assess the degree of eutrophication, acidification and damage by toxic chemicals (acid neutralising capacity, total phosphorus and dangerous substances). The classes are: excellent/good, fair, poor and seriously polluted.

River habitats

The natural habitat adjacent to a watercourse is an integral part of the aquatic environment. Hence, it is important that construction activities do not damage the river habitat as well as the water quality. Riverside habitats may be degraded by direct impacts, such as structural modifications to the banks, or by indirect impacts such as changes in land use resulting in modified runoff.

River Habitat Surveys (RHS) have been conducted by the environment regulator at 5600 sites throughout the UK and Isle of Man from 1994 to 1997 (Environment Agency, 1998b). The RHS assesses the physical qualities of a watercourse and any artificial modifications. One aspect of the survey is to determine the Habitat Modification Score (HMS) for each stretch of river. The HMS results in a series of habitat classes: semi-natural, predominantly unmodified, obviously modified, extensively modified and heavily modified. The surveys also include a Habitat Quality Assessment (HQA), which quantifies the "naturalness" of each site.

2.2.3   Groundwater

Impacts of pollution on groundwater are determined largely by the effect on industrial and, in particular, potable water supplies. Groundwaters are a preferable source of water abstraction in many regions because they need little treatment other than disinfection. The vulnerability of groundwater can be assessed using published vulnerability maps (Figure 2.2) and the source protection zones defined in the *Policy and practice for the protection of groundwater* (Environment Agency, 1998a) (Figure 2.3).

Pollution of groundwater is not as immediately apparent as that of surface waters. There are no immediate effects on flora and fauna nor are there visual signs to provoke "public awareness". Groundwater pollution is a serious problem because:

*   aquifer pollution persists for a long time because of the slow rate of water percolation through the aquifer

*   the pollution may remain unnoticed for some time, during which the polluting discharge might still be occurring

*   the natural processes that break down surface water pollution operate slowly if at all below ground

*   it is almost impossible to access the pollution in the aquifer or treat it *in situ*.

Unlike surface waters, sediments are not usually a hazard to groundwater as the particles are filtered out before the discharge reaches the water table. However, the downward flow of water may leach out pollutants from the ground and carry them to an underlying aquifer. Even at low concentrations, hydrocarbons can affect the odour and taste of groundwater, rendering it unsuitable for drinking water abstraction.

In some areas of the UK, reduced rates of water abstraction are causing groundwater levels to rise. This may lead to the re-mobilisation of contaminants and pollution of water in areas where high groundwater levels exist, or are likely to in the future. The problem is examined in *The engineering implications of rising groundwater levels in the deep aquifer beneath London* (CIRIA SP69, 1989) and *Rising groundwater levels in Birmingham and the engineering implications* (CIRIA SP92, 1993).

Dewatering operations, while not directly polluting the groundwater, can serve to draw in groundwater from the surrounding area. If contaminated groundwater is drawn towards an abstraction point near the site, it may pollute the water resource (see Case study 1). The contaminated water could reach the site itself, creating knock-on effects for discharge of the dewatered water. Contamination from organic pollutants presents one of the commonest forms of industrial pollution. It is quite likely that if organic pollutants exist near the site they will migrate towards the source of dewatering.

The over-abstraction of groundwaters in some coastal areas can result in the drawing-in of saline water, subsequently contaminating the supply. Fresh and saline waters in such areas are in delicate balance. The details of groundwater regimes are beyond the remit of this report, but it is important to recognise that the effects of changing the natural balance of groundwater recharge and migration are not easily, if at all, reversible.

A side effect of dewatering may be to lower groundwater levels in the land surrounding the construction site. This could lead to:

- settling of sensitive structures or services
- depletion of aquifer levels
- deterioration in groundwater quality.

The requirement to maintain groundwater levels at specific points may form one of the environment regulator's conditions for dewatering operations. Should this be the case, site water can typically be recharged either via recharge wells for large volumes or by infiltration through the ground. Should polluting material enter the dewatered excavation or be present on the ground, pollution will be carried directly to the aquifer in the recharged water.

As well as affecting the quality of groundwater for drinking purposes, pollution can affect groundwater-dependent habitats. This includes watercourses, springs and ponds that rely on groundwater baseflow, and plant species that obtain water and nutrients from shallow groundwater.

Case study 1 ☺   *Maintaining groundwater baseflow*

> At a large construction project near the Dorset coast, water was not allowed to be discharged onto the surrounding area due to the risk of damage to wildlife habitats caused by the associated mud. The water that filled excavations had to be removed from site by being pumped into a tanker. However, as removing this volume of rainwater could change the fresh/saline water balance and have harmful effects on trees and plants, provision was made to pump clean water into the excavation to recharge the underlying water table.

In some parts of the UK, including London, Birmingham and Liverpool, and areas where deep coal mining has ceased in recent years, groundwater is rising. Further guidance on this topic is given in *The engineering implications of rising groundwater levels in the deep aquifer beneath London* (CIRIA SP69, 1989) and *Rising groundwater levels in Birmingham and the engineering implications* (CIRIA SP92, 1993).

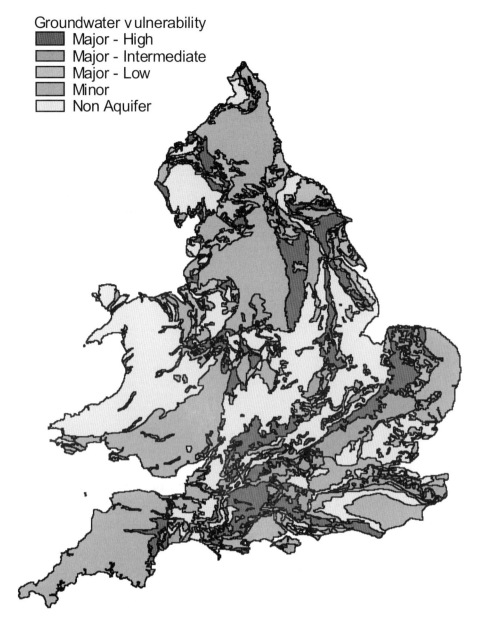

Figure 2.2   *Groundwater vulnerability for England and Wales (source: Environment Agency)*

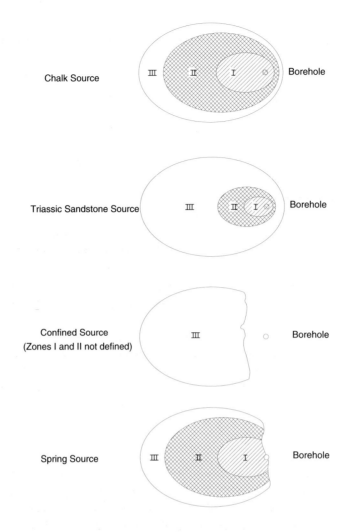

Figure 2.3   *Schematic diagram of source protection zones to assess groundwater vulnerability (source: Environment Agency)*

2.2.4   Mains and tankered water

Water may be brought intentionally onto site via the mains potable water supply or tankers, depending on the water use requirements. These sources of water should always be under the control of the site manager. Existing water supply pipes should be identified in the early stages of the site development to avoid the risk of accidental damage. The environment regulator should be consulted before any mains or tankered water, even if not contaminated, is discharged to local watercourses. The potable or tankered water supply may be from a source that is chemically different from that of the local watercourse. For example, the imported supply may be from an upland reservoir with a low pH and the local watercourse might be a chalk stream with a high pH and a different ecology. Water from the mains supply will also have undergone chlorination. A large input of water from a significantly different source could have a detrimental impact on the fauna and flora.

2.3 NATURAL WATER PROPERTIES AND POLLUTANTS

Brief descriptors of some of the most commonly discussed properties of natural waterbodies are given below. Also included are those pollutants that are relevant to construction site activities. Note that some substances can be classed as both naturally occurring and a pollutant, depending on their source, final location and concentration. For the purpose of this book, a pollutant is defined as a substance that occurs either in a location where it is not naturally occurring or in an abnormally high concentration.

Dissolved oxygen

Dissolved oxygen (DO) is essential for aquatic organisms. It is consumed by degradation of organic matter (sewage, dead algae, food processing waste etc) and by the respiration of organisms. The major source of oxygen to the water column is through contact with the atmosphere and diffusion rates are increased by water turbulence. The solubility of oxygen decreases with both increasing temperature and dissolved salt concentration.

The impact of discharges that remove oxygen from the water column can vary according to the status of the receiving water. For example, if water temperatures are high and dissolved oxygen concentrations are low (a common seasonal effect), a further reduction in DO resulting from a discharge might significantly affect aquatic organisms that are already under stress. DO is used as a water quality indicator.

Biochemical oxygen demand (BOD)

Biochemical oxygen demand (BOD) is a water quality indicator that measures the potential impact of organic matter on dissolved oxygen in a waterbody. As organic matter is degraded by micro-organisms, oxygen is consumed by their metabolic processes. The measurement of BOD has been standardised as the quantity of oxygen consumed in a sample of water by selected micro-organisms over a five-day period at 20° C. High BOD is indicative of poor water quality. BOD limits are often set for discharges with a high organic matter content, for example sewage discharges.

Chemical oxygen demand (COD)

Chemical oxygen demand (COD) is a water quality indicator and is a measure of the oxygen required for the chemical oxidation of compounds (organic and inorganic) within the water column. It cannot differentiate between organic and inorganic material. Sources of COD include sewage discharges and industrial effluents. Typically, COD limits have been applied to industrial effluents as a method of control.

Ammonia

Ammonia occurs in waterbodies from both natural and anthropogenic sources (industrial and sewage). It is produced as the initial product of decay for nitrogenous organic wastes and is toxic to aquatic organisms. It is a List II substance as defined by the Groundwater Regulations and Dangerous Substances Regulations of the UK (see Sections 3.2.2 and 3.2.3).

Acidity, alkalinity and pH

In terms of natural waters and wastewaters, acidity can be defined as the capacity of water to neutralise hydroxide ions (OH^-) and alkalinity as the capacity to neutralise hydrogen ions (H^+) (Manahan, 1994). pH is a measure of the balance of hydroxide and hydrogen ions in a given solution. A high concentration of hydrogen ions (and low concentration of hydroxide ions) represents an acidic solution and low pH (pH < 7). A low concentration of hydrogen ions (and high concentration of hydroxide ions) represents an alkaline solution and high pH (pH > 7). A neutral solution has the same concentration of hydrogen ions and hydroxide ions and has a pH of 7, for example, distilled water.

Acidity is controlled by naturally occurring weak acids, such as carbonic, humic and fulvic acids, and strong mineral acids from acidic metal ions (such as iron). Alkalinity is generally controlled by the concentrations of bicarbonate, carbonate and hydroxide, which are usually associated with calcium, magnesium, sodium and potassium salts. Other compounds, such as borate, phosphate and silicates, may also contribute to alkalinity (Chapman, 1996). In addition, the actions of algae and bacteria can also influence the pH of a waterbody.

The pH of natural waters is generally in the range 6.0–8.5. There are ranges of pH that aquatic organisms can tolerate even though they are not optimal conditions for growth, but beyond this mortality occurs. Most fish species die once the pH drops to 4.5–5.0 (Kotz and Purcell, 1987).

Industrial wastes, acid mine drainage and acid rainfall are the commonest contributors to acidity in natural waters. Excess alkalinity is often caused by discharges of cement and caustic compounds (see Case study 2).

Case study 2 ⊗   *Alkaline discharge contaminates potable water*

In 1995, a water company began commissioning a cement-lined main that had not been used since it was built in the 1970s. Intending to flush it out, the pipe was filled with water, as it was believed to be isolated from the rest of the supply system. It was not, and flush water seeped into the drinking water supply. Some 20 complaints were received from customers. Water was found to be alkaline, with a pH of 12.2; in another case a pH of 10.3 was found. The legal standard is for pH to be between 5.5 and 9.5. The high pH resulted from contact between the water and cement in the main. The company was charged under Section 70 of WIA 1991 of supplying unfit water. It pleaded guilty and was fined £8000, with £3000 costs imposed.

Source: Environ Law Mgmt 9(5) Sep–Oct 1997

Hardness

The hardness of natural waters is a function of the concentration of calcium and magnesium salts in solution. It is measured as mass of calcium carbonate ($CaCO_3$) per litre. Total hardness of a waterbody is the sum of "temporary" and "permanent" hardness. Temporary or carbonate hardness is derived from calcium and magnesium hydrocarbonates, and permanent or non-carbonate hardness is the result of calcium and magnesium salts of strong acids (chlorides and sulphates). Temporary hardness can be removed by boiling, which causes the precipitation of the carbonates.

The hardness of a waterbody affects the toxicity of other compounds to aquatic organisms. For example, zinc becomes more toxic to fish as the hardness decreases, so more stringent water quality standards for zinc apply in waters with low hardness.

Sediments, suspended particles and turbidity

Sediments are defined in categories from clay, silt and sand to gravel and larger by the Udden-Wentworth grain size scale (Table 2.2). Suspended particulate matter (SPM) in natural waterbodies is defined as material that will not pass through a filter of pore size 0.45 μm and is less than 63 μm. SPM can be composed of inorganic particles (such as mineral silts and clays) or organic particles such as plankton or organic matter.

Sand and gravels are only suspended in periods of high water velocity. They move by bouncing and rolling along the river bed (saltation). The term "clay" describes both a particle size and a group of microcrystalline minerals (eg illite, kaolinite and montmorillonite).

The phi scale (ϕ) is a logarithmic scale used to define the size of particles and is derived by $\phi = -\log_2$ (size in mm) (Dyer, 1986).

Table 2.2 *Udden–Wentworth grain size scale*

Category	Phi	Grain size
Clay	>8 ϕ	<4 μm
Silt	4–8 ϕ	4–63 μm
Sand	-1–4 ϕ	64 μm–2 mm
Gravel	<-1 ϕ	>2 mm

The particle size of sediment is a major factor in its environmental impact, influencing the treatment methods needed to clean up discharges. Fine particles take a long time to settle out and consequently are difficult to remove with a standard settlement tank. This trait means that they can have an impact a great distance downstream of the discharge. Coarse particles are easier to settle out of suspension but can cause a greater impact at the discharge point (for example, bank scouring and sedimentation of the stream bed).

SPM can also act as a medium for the transportation of other compounds such as nutrients, heavy metals (lead, zinc, mercury, cadmium etc), metalloids (such as arsenic) and hydrophobic organic pollutants (for example, dioxins and PCBs), which adsorb onto the surface of the particle. The clay fraction (<63 μm) has the highest surface area to volume ratio of the sediment categories. Therefore, for a given mass of suspended particles, the concentration of pollutants will be higher in clay than, for example, in gravels. Research has shown that the clay fraction is the most significant for the transport of pollutants (Luker and Montague, 1994). Typically 70–77 per cent of hydrocarbons show a strong attachment to suspended solids. If the solids are removed, therefore, the hydrocarbon pollution in the water is also significantly reduced.

Abnormal discharges of solids to a watercourse, apart from any toxic compounds associated with them, can also have a detrimental impact on aquatic organisms by:

- clogging the gills of fish so they suffocate and die
- covering spawning sites to form thick sediments, leading to permanent loss of reeds
- injuring fish by abrasive action
- destroying flora and fauna, for example by destroying insect habitats on the riverbed, thus starving fish of their food source
- stunting aquatic plant growth by limiting oxygen supplies, shelter and food sources
- building up to cause flooding
- affecting industrial or potable water abstractions.

Fine-grained suspended sediments in discharge water may require flocculants to aid settlement. However, these should be used with care and only after consultation with the appropriate environment regulator because of their potential to cause pollution.

Turbidity is the measure of light-scattering and absorption within the water column resulting from SPM (see Case study 3). Turbidity can be measured using a turbidity meter that provides readings in nephelometric turbidity units (NTU). Changes in turbidity can be due to the presence of either organic (phytoplankton bloom or sewage discharge) or inorganic (surface runoff or discharges from construction sites) particles.

Case study 3 ⊗   *Suspended solids damage watercourse*

> The defendant, a contractor on a large housing development, was installing storm-water tanks to prevent flooding, and excavated a large hole for this purpose. Clean water was pumped out of this hole, but a separate pump was needed for water at the bottom. The water was heavy with silt and it was pumped into a controlled water, making it white and turbid for 2 km. The company was fined £1000, with £3000 costs.
>
> *Source: Environ Law Mgmt 10(2) Mar–Apr 1998*

Heavy metals and metalloids

Heavy metals (such as lead, zinc, mercury and cadmium) and metalloids (such as arsenic) may be present in silt originating from contaminated ground or naturally metalliferous ground conditions. The solubility of metals and metalloids tends to be highest and hence more toxic in low-pH or "soft" water areas (see Section 2.4.4). Dissolved lead is a serious and accumulative poison. Low concentrations may affect tadpoles, frogs and fish such as minnows, stickleback and trout (0.1–6.4 mg/l may be toxic; Luker and Montague, 1994). However, lead has a low solubility, so its actual environmental impact is less than might be expected. Fish are also particularly sensitive to dissolved copper and zinc at levels less than 1 mg/l. It is important to prevent heavy metals from entering the human food chain.

Some metals and metalloids are classified by the Groundwater Regulations and Dangerous Substances Regulations as List I and List II substances because of their toxic effects (see Sections 3.2.2 and 3.2.3). These regulations either prevent (List I) or limit (List II) the discharge of these metals to the aquatic environment.

Iron can be a very visible, if non-toxic, pollutant. It is a common oxidation product of naturally occurring pyrites, resulting in thick red-brown deposits typical of mine water discharges. The freshly precipitated iron hydroxide can form highly reactive coatings on particles, causing other compounds to adsorb onto the surface of the particle. Trace metals such as lead, manganese, cadmium and arsenic can be adsorbed onto these reactive surfaces, and the removal of these particles can benefit water quality.

Conductivity and salinity

Conductivity is a measure of the ability of a solution to conduct electricity and is proportional to the concentration of dissolved mineral salts. The units are microsiemens per centimetre (μS/cm). In freshwater, conductivity can be used to indicate pollution, such as land runoff, road salting and industrial discharges. Conductivity also varies with temperature.

Salinity refers to the quantities of dissolved ions in seawater that are in constant relative proportion, and can be calculated from conductivity. Low-salinity waters can be found at the river end-point of estuaries where mixing between freshwater and seawater occurs. However, at low salinities the proportion of dissolved ions detected may change because of land-based sources of conductivity and the relationship between salinity and conductivity breaks down.

Mineral oils and petroleum products

Mineral oils and petroleum products are complex mixtures of hydrocarbons. These compounds can form surface films as thin as one molecule thick, thus enabling a small oil spillage to cover a large surface area. For example, an oil spillage of 1 litre is sufficient to contaminate 1 million litres of water to a level where it is unfit to drink (SEPA, 1998). Oils also bind to the surface of sediments, strata and organisms (for example causing oiling on marine birds). Some types of oil will also disperse throughout the water column by forming an emulsion. Concentrations of crude oil in excess of 0.3 mg/l can prove toxic to freshwater fish (Chapman, 1996).

Even at low concentrations, hydrocarbons can cause an impact because they give rise to a visible sheen on the water surface and exert an oxygen demand. The adverse taste and odour may make the water unsuitable for human consumption or industrial production. Persistent and non-persistent mineral oils and hydrocarbons are List I and II substances, respectively, as defined by the Groundwater Regulations and the Dangerous Substances Regulations (see Sections 3.2.2 and 3.2.3). As such, their release to the environment is controlled. An example of the impact of oil pollution from a construction site is given in Case study 4.

Case study 4 ⊗   *Poor equipment maintenance results in red diesel leakage*

Following public complaint, Agency staff found oil in a river downstream of the defendant's site. This site was inspected and puddles of red diesel were found beneath two tanks. On the next day oil was found in a culvert entering from a pipe, which was traced back to a tank on the defendant's site. Oil was pumped between the two tanks, and if the valves between them were not locked there could be an escape. The company had come to the Agency's attention five times before. It was charged under Section 85(1) and (6) of WRA 1991 and pleaded guilty. The company was fined £12 000 with costs.

Source: Environ Law Mgmt 10(5) Sept–Oct 1998

Colour, visual impact and odour

The colour of water is determined by the effect of dissolved and suspended particles on the absorption of light. Colour can be affected by both natural processes (such as algal blooms and runoff from peat uplands) and anthropogenic activities (such as industrial effluents). It is measured in platinum-cobalt units and is determined by comparison with standard dilutions of platinum and cobalt compounds.

The visual impact of a discharge may affect more than colour. For example, high suspended solids, precipitates, scums, litter and floating solids will all reduce the aesthetic quality of a natural waterbody.

Odour can result from both natural and anthropogenic sources. Industrial discharges may have odour problems directly associated with them or may generate unpleasant odours during biological decomposition.

Water temperature

The discharge of water into a waterbody or watercourse whose temperature is higher or lower than that of the receiving water is termed thermal pollution. The scale of the pollution will depend on parameters including:

- temperature difference between the discharge and the receiving water
- volume of the discharge proportional to the receiving water
- timing and duration of discharge.

A change in the ambient temperature of a waterbody, even of one or two degrees, can exert significant effects on the organisms within the water, particularly on fish.

Fish differ in their tolerance to temperature outside their preferred range depending on species, stage of development, acclimation temperature, dissolved oxygen, pollution and season. Juvenile and adult fish can tolerate a wider range of temperature than fry and embryos. When the ambient water temperature is outside the preferred range, feeding, growth and reproductive success may be affected.

An increase in temperature also decreases the solubility of oxygen in water, and it may be this secondary effect, rather than the elevated temperature itself, which most significantly affects the health of the fish. The same factor may also have serious effects on the invertebrates and aquatic plants within a waterbody.

Herbicides

Herbicides used on site for site clearance may enter waterbodies or watercourses either directly or as runoff following rainfall (see Case study 5). Formal approval is required for the use of herbicides in or near controlled waters. Only herbicides from an approved list are acceptable and their use must be in accordance with the manufacturer's product label. Incorrect use of herbicides may kill aquatic plants and animals. This can also have indirect impacts on the waterbody, including:

- water quality changes – the decay of large quantities of aquatic plant and/or animal matter killed by herbicides may lead to significant short-term changes in water quality. Bacteria that break down the plant and animal matter use large quantities of oxygen. This may cause oxygen levels within the waterbody to drop dramatically and result in fish kills. High levels of nutrients may be released during the decaying process, which may lead to the growth of sewage fungus or algal blooms
- loss of habitat for aquatic invertebrates – aquatic plants provide predation refuges for aquatic invertebrates such as waterfleas (Daphnia spp). If the plants are destroyed, these invertebrates, which graze on phytoplankton (floating, unicellular plants), have little refuge from fish predators (Moss 1992). The loss of the inverte-brates may allow the phytoplankton community to establish, thus creating shade and preventing the re-establishment of the aquatic plant beds
- loss of fish habitat – many species of fish may lay their eggs among beds of aquatic plants and loss of these beds may preclude breeding success for these species. Other species, eg Pike (*Esox lucius*), hide among aquatic plant beds to ambush prey. If the aquatic plants are removed, the hunting success of these species may be severely affected, such that the species is no longer able to survive within that waterbody
- the use of herbicides in aquatic systems needs the approval of the environment regulator. Only approved products may be used (details should be obtained from the environment regulator). A Ministry of Agriculture, Fisheries and Food publication (MAFF, 1991) provides details on the correct usage of herbicides and pesticides

with regard to watercourses and groundwater, as well as guidance on the storage, application and disposal of pesticides. More detailed information is provided in another MAFF document (MAFF and HSC, 1990).

Case study 5 ⊗   *Herbicide stored adjacent to drains results in pollution*

A company reported a loss of herbicide from its site, and consequent pollution of a watercourse. The container of herbicide had been stored in an area mistakenly thought to be isolated from surface water drains. The container had leaked into the drains and the material had thence escaped to a watercourse – a case of poor site management. A charge was brought against the company under section 85(1) of WRA 1991. The company pleaded guilty and was fined £2000 with costs.

Source: Environ Law Mgmt 9(5) Sep–Oct 1997

Synergistic/additive effects

Certain pollutants when discharged into the aquatic environment may act in a synergistic way, ie their combined toxicity to freshwater organisms such as fish may be greater than the sum of their individual effects. This is the case with (but not restricted to) the following combinations: ammonia and copper; copper and cadmium; copper, zinc and nickel (Alabaster *et al*, 1987).

Other pollutants when discharged into an aquatic environment may have an undesirable effect on other water quality parameters. These include:

- elevated water temperature – the solubility of oxygen in water decreases with increasing temperature. This reduces the amount of oxygen available to aquatic organisms, potentially placing them under stress

- discharge of silt and organic matter to watercourses – the discharge of particulate matter to a waterbody can directly affect aquatic organisms by causing abrasive tissue damage, particularly to gill tissues. In addition, if organic-rich particulate matter is discharged to a waterbody, dissolved oxygen concentrations can fall as the organic material is broken down by bacteria. This will decrease the oxygen available to other aquatic organisms, potentially placing them under stress. The nutrients nitrogen and phosphorus may be released into the water following the breakdown of organic material. This may lead to hypernutrification (an excess of nutrients within the water) and eutrophication, causing algal blooms or excessive aquatic plant growth (macrophytes). The decomposition of these plants following the growing season may also lead to shortages of dissolved oxygen within the water

- discharge of oil/diesel into a waterbody – in addition to the direct toxic effects that diesel or oil may have on aquatic organisms, the process of breakdown of these compounds by bacteria will decrease the dissolved oxygen available for aquatic organisms, potentially leading to stress

- sewage effluents discharged into watercourses – the high organic load of sewage will cause dissolved oxygen in the water to decrease as the sewage is broken down by bacteria, decreasing the amount available to aquatic organisms. The high ammonia content of sewage can be toxic to aquatic organisms, particularly in conditions of low dissolved oxygen. Following the breakdown of the organic matter, nutrients released in the water column can lead to eutrophication and its associated problems (see above).

2.4   SOURCES OF WATER POLLUTION

Pollution of water on construction sites can occur following the release into, or formation of, the following types of pollutant: suspended solids, oils, hydrocarbons, concrete, cement products, heavy metals, metalloids, bentonite, sewage, pesticides, herbicides, hazardous materials and temperature.

2.4.1   Suspended solids

By far the most common instance of water pollution from construction activities is suspended sediments (see Case study 6). Sources of suspended sediment pollution include:

- excavations
- exposed ground and stockpiles
- plant and wheel washing
- build-up of dust and mud on site roads
- disturbance of river bed or banks
- deposition/storage of waste materials in watercourses
- pumping of contaminated surface waters or groundwaters accumulated on the construction site directly into controlled waters.

Case study 6 ⊗   *Suspended sediments from site contaminate watercourse*

> Following public complaint Agency staff found that a brook was heavily discoloured and water contaminated with sediment that had been discharged from the defendant's construction site; no measures had been taken to prevent sediment entering the site drainage system. The company was charged under section 85(1) of WRA 1991 and following a guilty plea a total fine and costs of £8373 was awarded.
>
> *Source: Environ Law Mgmt 10(5) Sept–Oct 1998*

2.4.2   Oils and hydrocarbons

Oil is the second most common pollutant from construction sites in terms of numbers of incidents. Use of diesel, lubricating oil, fuel oil, petrol and hydraulic fluids all entail a risk of spillage or leakage. Table 2.3 gives the major potential sources of oil pollution.

Table 2.3   *Sources of oil pollution*

Activity	Problem
Storage tanks	Leaking valves
	Leaking pipework
	Corrosion
	Frost damage
General use and maintenance	Refuelling
	Leaking pumps, bowsers, generators
	Disposal of waste oil
Accident	Spillage (greatest risk during refuelling)
	Mechanical failure, eg rupture of hydraulic pipes
	Inadequate bunding of storage area or tank
	Vandalism

Measures can be taken to prevent oil becoming a pollutant. In most cases, leakage of oil is avoidable through regular checks for signs of wear and tear on plant and tanks. Vandalism can be prevented by secure protection of storage compounds, hoses, trigger guns and plant. Environment Agency/SEPA/EHS guidelines (PPG5) state that the greatest risk of spillage is during refuelling (see Case study 7). Designated areas should be used for refuelling and storage of oil and machinery. The methods required to minimise the risk of oil pollution are described in detail in Section 6.

Case study 7 ⊗   *Construction company fined for causing oil pollution*

In November 1997 oil was delivered to a 6000 l oil storage tank serving warm-air blowers on a construction site in Raynesway, Derbyshire. The following day the construction company discovered that oil had been lost from the system. Believing that the oil had entered the foul sewer, the company immediately notified Severn Trent Water, which informed the Environment Agency. The investigating officer found neat red diesel flowing from a surface water sewer serving the site, and accumulating in pools along the river margin, with iridescence covering the river surface. Inspection of the site revealed that a tap fitted on the oil distribution system had been opened, allowing approximately 5000 l of oil to escape.

Oil had affected 20 km of river, including a major recreational fishery. Severn Trent Water's drinking water abstraction at Church Wilne, some 15 km downstream, was also affected.

Derby magistrates fined the construction company £13 000, and the Environment Agency recovered costs of £2700 for installing oil booms.

Source: Environment Agency, 1998b

2.4.3   Concrete and cement products

The use of concrete and cement products on site can present a contamination risk because of the potential for uncontrolled release of washdown water/runoff. Where on-site concrete production takes place, a large volume of wastewater can be generated, particularly from washing out concrete batching plant. Where concrete is brought to site, the washing of ready-mix lorries can create a similar source of pollution.

If these activities are not carried out in a designated area, wastewater may enter the aquatic environment without treatment. Spillages from concrete pours are also likely to be hosed down, thus potentially entering the drainage system. Uncontrolled use of wet concrete in close proximity to watercourses can pose a particularly serious hazard.

2.4.4   Heavy metals and metalloids

Some metals are potentially more damaging than others when present in the aquatic environment (see Section 2.3). Additionally, many metals are also toxic to humans so should not be allowed to enter the food chain. The solubility of metals within controlled waters is usually a function of the pH of the discharge and/or the acidity of the receiving waters. Construction activities within ground that has a naturally high metal content may, if the ground is disturbed, produce a higher concentration of metals in any site water. The exposure of materials with a high metal content, such as contaminated ground, may result in oxidation of the material and the collection of a highly visible, as well as potentially polluting, volume of water.

2.4.5 Bentonite

The use of bentonite may cause pollution incidents. The spillage or discharge of bentonite may contaminate local watercourses and block local drainage systems. In addition, the use of bentonite within the ground may pollute the water table, with consequential transport of the contamination through the aquifer.

2.4.6 Other pollutants and hazardous materials

There is a potential pollution hazard from the use and uncontrolled release of substances such as material blown from rubbish storage areas or stockpiles, solvents, cleaning agents, detergents, paint, adhesives, sealant, drilling fluids, herbicides and other chemicals on sites. In the absence of correct procedures for delivery, storage, use and clean-up of these substances, the potential consequences of such a spillage on site can be very serious (see Case study 8).

Case study 8 ☹   *Timber preservative incorrectly contained results in pollution*

> A company reported a spill of timber preservative on its site. The company thought that it was contained behind a bund wall, but on inspection this was found to have no inner lining and preservative had seeped through into a controlled water. As a result, extensive ameliorative action had to be taken. A charge was brought under section 85(1) of WRA 1991. The company pleaded guilty and was fined £6000 with costs.
>
> *Source: Environ Law Mgmt 9(5) Sep–Oct 1997*

2.4.7 Contaminated ground

Contaminated ground presents particular problems. Suspended sediments, generated from the sources described in Section 2.4.1, pose further pollution hazards if generated from contaminated ground. Disturbance of the ground may result in rainfall or groundwater inflow mobilising contaminants, thereby increasing the likelihood of pollution of surface or groundwater. Existing contaminated groundwater at a site presents a hazard to watercourses even if no siteworks are carried out. Construction activities such as dewatering could significantly increase the risk to the aquatic environment. Disturbance of contaminated groundwater by dewatering or other processes may result in the environment regulator having to implement clean-up measures.

2.4.8 Indicators of pollution

Construction site staff should be aware of the following indicators of water pollution. If such indicators are observed, further investigation should be undertaken:

- change in water colour
- change in water transparency
- oily sheen to water surface
- floating detritus
- scums and foams
- dead/decaying fauna and/or flora.

2.5	**POLLUTION PATHWAYS**

This section highlights the "pathways" through which pollutants can enter the water environment on construction sites, that is, site runoff, dewatering operations, vertical migration into groundwater (infiltration) and direct input.

2.5.1	**Site runoff**

In developed areas, surface water runoff may be carried by surface water drains directly to a receiving waterbody such as a river or stream. Pollutants on the surface of the ground or entering the drainage system serving the site can be discharged directly into a watercourse.

Foul water is treated at a wastewater treatment works before discharge. However, this treatment is specific to the normal content of the wastewater and may not remove oil or chemicals. The consent of the sewerage undertaker will be required before discharge to any wastewater treatment system can take place. In some areas, surface and foul sewerage are combined and both loads pass to wastewater treatment works. In these cases, consideration should be given to the volume of water entering the drain to avoid overloading the system and potentially causing a stormwater overflow (see Case study 9). Combined sewer overflows (CSOs) are designed to discharge stormwater runoff which is too great to go to the wastewater treatment works. CSOs are designed with the consent of the environment regulator and enable the sewerage undertaker to discharge under storm conditions untreated, but very dilute, effluent directly to a watercourse. The CSOs are consented to function only under storm events of a specified duration and intensity. Uncontrolled discharge to sewer from a construction site (eg from storm runoff or a large spill) may result in the CSO operating outside the terms of its consent.

Case study 9 ⊗   *Escape of oil into storm drains*

> After heavy rainfall a company's surface water drains failed, so that oil overflowed into a storm drain and thence into a controlled water. The volume of water had overwhelmed the on-site drains. A charge of allowing pollution of controlled waters was brought, resulting in a fine of £2000, with costs of £2370.
>
> *Source: Environ Law Mgmt 9(5) Sep–Oct 1997*

Pollution of surface runoff can be caused by rainfall washing away solids and/or liquids accumulated on the ground or by deliberately hosing down a spill. This pathway can be restricted at source both by preventing contamination of the ground surface by suitable delivery, storage and usage procedures (Section 5), and by treating the runoff using interceptors, settlement tanks or filters (Section 6) before discharge to a waterway.

Detergents are not suitable for discharge to surface drains, even if described as biodegradable, so such activities should be carried out in bunded/contained designated areas that drain to the foul sewer (subject to approval of the local sewerage undertaker). Alternatively, recirculating or closed-cycle vehicle wash systems are available. Further guidance is available from PPG 13, *The use of high pressure water and stream cleaners*.

Suspended solids are the main pollutant from construction sites, one of the major sources of which is erosion of exposed soils. Removal of surface cover, including roofs, floor slabs, vegetation and topsoil, allows rainfall and site water to erode the exposed subsoils, causing large quantities of silt to be mobilised in surface runoff. McNeill (1996) highlighted the case of runoff during six motorway construction projects within the catchment of two rivers. Stripping the development area resulted in discharges containing large quantities of suspended solids, which led to the downgrading of the class of the rivers and subsequent contractors' fines of £10 000–£40 000.

Stockpiles of imported or excavated material can be eroded in a similar manner, so should be kept covered or contained. A build-up of dust and mud deposits on haul roads also results in silt-laden runoff following rainfall.

It is important to consider the chemical composition of natural soils or made-up ground such as slag that is to be excavated or could be eroded. Tests on carboniferous rocks containing pyrite minerals (metal sulphides) before the start of a construction project in Devon (Institution of Civil Engineers, 1990) showed that oxidation of the pyrite in the presence of water produced acidic water containing iron and manganese. This is similar to the widely known red-brown acid mine water discharges and associated thick red-brown deposits in watercourses.

Where removal or excavation of contaminated material is required, this can expose relatively fresh areas of contamination that may be susceptible to oxidation or leaching. Heavy rainfall or ingress of groundwater in these excavations can result in pollution entering surface water systems or underlying aquifers.

Treatment of contaminated ground, such as the use of microbiological degradation, may also present a short-term risk to groundwater quality unless adequate precautions, such as lining the site, are taken.

2.5.2   Dewatering operations

Groundwater control operations are a probable main cause of water pollution from construction sites. The environmental problems associated with groundwater control operations are discussed in *Groundwater control – design and practice* (CIRIA C515, 2000a). Those relevant to water pollution are summarised in Table 2.4.

Table 2.4   *Potential pollution resulting from groundwater control operations*

Potential problem	Source of problem
Potential problems from pumping out (abstracting) groundwater	• Migration of contaminated groundwater from adjacent sites • Saline intrusion • Derogation of groundwater sources
Potential problems from discharge	• Discharge of water containing a high suspended solids concentration • Discharge of contaminated water from an unidentified source or as a result of migration • Erosion of the river bank and scouring of watercourses • Discharge of acidic groundwater to surface watercourses resulting in precipitation of metals (eg iron) and calcium carbonate, and changes in pH, hardness, BOD and COD

Groundwater abstraction

A direct result of dewatering operations is the removal of groundwater from the surrounding area and the potential creation of new hydraulic gradients that may induce new flow patterns. Leaks in existing underground tanks may also occur as a result of pressure gradient changes. In some cases, this water may be contaminated by activities at an adjacent site, such as a landfill. In coastal or estuarine areas, the lowering of water tables may encourage saline intrusion inland. Over-abstraction could also result in the lowering of surface water levels.

Discharge of groundwater

Groundwater control operations are a major source of silt pollution. Excavations below the water table will result in large volumes of water requiring discharge. As a result of both the excavation work and the washing-out of fine material by inflowing groundwater, the discharge water will contain a high level of suspended solids.

If waters collected at a site are discharged directly to a watercourse and at a high rate, the river bank or bed could be disturbed and eroded, resulting in the river water being contaminated by suspended sediment. Furthermore, the erosion or scouring action can cause long-term damage to the watercourse itself (see Case study 10).

Restricting the pathway for pollution can take two forms. The first is limiting the groundwater inflow into excavations. This is beneficial, as it reduces the volume of wastewater requiring discharge and decreases the likelihood of groundwater migration off site. Although in practice this is possible to achieve, there is a significant cost. The second method is to isolate and contain sources of contamination on site to ensure that no pollution reaches excavations via site runoff.

Case study 10 ⊗   *Unconsented discharge from dewatering process*

While construction work took place on a road culvert, a discharge from a dewatering works entered a controlled water. A charge was brought under section 85(1) of WRA and the company was fined £5000 with costs.

Source: Environ Law Mgmt 9(5) Sep–Oct 1997

2.5.3   Vertical migration into groundwater/infiltration

Surface spills of pollutants onto the ground at a site have the potential to migrate downwards to the water table. The ease with which unacceptable effects on groundwater resources can occur can is termed "groundwater vulnerability". The vulnerability of a resource to a particular pollutant threat depends on the characteristics of the soils at the site, the nature of the underlying geology and the depth of the water table (Environment Agency, 1998a). It is also affected by the quality of the existing groundwater and its use. Highly permeable soils overlying permeable bedrock and a shallow water table provide an easy and rapid pathway to the groundwater. An impermeable surface or impermeable strata and a deep water table inhibit the pathway to the groundwater.

Piling, in particular vibro-replacement piles (Taylor *et al*, 1995; National Rivers Authority, 1994), forms a direct flow pathway down columns of granular material for contaminated water and leachates to potentially move into an underlying aquifer both during and after construction. If the piles break through a naturally impermeable horizon, perched groundwater in a higher horizon may also flow vertically.

2.5.4   Direct input

Construction works within or adjacent to watercourses are at high risk of causing pollution. Excavations of the river bed or banks can generate silty water as the excavated and exposed materials are washed downstream. In such cases, any spillage or leakage of wet concrete or fuel oils directly into controlled waters will limit the use of any runoff treatments recommended for "inland" construction sites (see Section 6.1.5). As there is little that can be done to restrict pollution pathways in this situation, it is necessary either to remove or at least reduce the risk of pollution at source.

During construction work on bridges (see Section 6.2.1) or other structures over or adjacent to a watercourse, physical methods of cleaning or surface preparation should be adopted, where possible, in preference to the use of liquid chemical products containing caustic or acidic solutions etc. Solid by-products such as leaded paint dust and fragments resulting from cleaning and preparation processes should be controlled.

Where a small watercourse such as a stream or ditch crosses a construction site, its presence is sometimes overlooked. Movement of site plant and dumping of construction debris across the stream will result in deterioration of its water quality and physical nature, as well as that of any larger stream or river into which it subsequently flows.

2.6 WATER POLLUTION INCIDENTS

Aqueous discharges from a construction site will ultimately end up in a surface waterbody (lake, canal or river) or in a groundwater system either directly from site or indirectly via a treatment system. The definition of a pollution incident for the purpose of this book is an unconsented discharge or a discharge in breach of an existing consent.

The impact of pollution on the water environment will depend on the type and quantity or concentration of the pollutant and the sensitivity of the waterbody (see Case study 11). The magnitude of a pollution incident can be classified by the environment regulator's prosecution policy, which also serves to highlight the environmental impact of pollution.

Case study 11 ☹   *Surface water discharges from construction site*

> In January 1996, Environment Agency environmental protection officers inspecting the Walsall Canal at Wednesbury saw that it was discoloured. About 1 km of the canal was coloured red with what proved to be clay particles. This discoloration was traced to a site where two construction companies were operating.
>
> A bund had been built around the site to prevent surface water runoff, but this had been breached at one point. This was allowing water contaminated with clay to run into the canal. On another part of the site, a pump was found to be discharging water contaminated with clay into an inadequate settlement tank, with an overflow of polluted water into a highway drain discharging to the Lea Brook. Both companies were prosecuted and each fined £2500.
>
> *Source: Environment Agency (1998b)*

Water pollution incidents in England, Wales and Northern Ireland

Definitions for the severity of water pollution incidents vary slightly between Northern Ireland and England/Wales, but are based on the same principles, with four major categories of incident: major, significant, minor and no impact.

From 1 January 1999, the Environment Agency modified its approach to the categorisation of pollution incidents. It has developed the common incident classification system (CICS), a two-tiered methodology that identifies separately the *potential* of an incident to pollute and the *actual* impact caused. This system takes into account the amount of work that the Agency undertakes to stop a pollution incident from having a major impact on the environment. If a major incident has been contained successfully and had minimal impact on the environment, its significance as an unacceptable event is not diminished by this new categorisation system. Since April 1995 the Agency has endeavoured to recover the costs involved in cleaning up pollution incidents under the "polluter pays" principle", irrespective of any legal action.

The list below gives the EA environmental impact criteria for water pollution incidents:

Category 1 (major)

- persistent and extensive effects on water quality
- major damage to the aquatic ecosystem
- closure of a potable abstraction point
- major impact on amenity value
- major damage to agriculture/commerce
- serious impact on people

Category 2 (significant)

- significant effect on water quality
- significant damage to the aquatic ecosystem
- non-routine notification of potable abstractors
- reduction in amenity value
- damage to agriculture or commerce
- impact on people

Category 3 (minor)

- minimal effect on water quality
- minor damage to the aquatic ecosystem
- amenity value only marginally affected
- minimal impact on agriculture/commerce

Category 4 (no impact)

- no impact.

Water pollution incidents in Scotland

In Scotland, pollution incidents are categorised first by sector (industrial, agricultural or other) and then by type of pollution (see Table 2.5). The incidents are further divided into routine incidents and significant incidents. Pollution from construction sites is not identified separately from other industrial sources.

Table 2.5   *Water pollution incident classification system in Scotland*

Sector	Classification	Sector	Classification
Industrial	Pollution by oil – tidal waters	Other	Pollution by sewage
	Pollution by oil – inland spills		Pollution by refuse
	Pollution by mineral solids		Pollution by tip leachate
	Pollution by trade effluent		Pollution by oil – tidal waters
	Pollution by chemicals		Pollution by oil – inland spills
	Pollution by fish farm effluent		Pollution by chemicals
	Effluent from paper mills		Naturally occurring pollution
	Other		Undetermined
Agricultural	Leaking silo		Other
	Leaking silage effluent tank		
	Escape of animal slurry		
	Pollution by chemicals		
	Pollution by fuel oil		
	Farm drainage		
	Other		

Water pollution incidents in Jersey and Guernsey

In Jersey the Pollution (Jersey) Law was passed in late 1999 and will come into force by the end of 2000. The Department of Public Services provides practical assistance and should be contacted in the event of an incident.

There is a Pollution Hotline, manned during work hours, with an answerphone out of hours. The Department of Public Services undertakes water quality sampling as needed following incidents.

There are only a few streams in Guernsey and there are no lakes or major rivers. If a pollution incident occurs within the catchment area of the State of Guernsey Waterboard (which covers the majority of the island, except for a small area around the perimeter of the island), it is investigated by the water board. If a pollution incident occurs outside the catchment area, it is investigated by the Public Services Department (possibly by the Environmental Health section, if there is any human health implication).

Water pollution incidents on the Isle of Man

Pollution incidents on the Isle of Man are investigated either by the Department of Environmental Health or the Department of Agriculture (Fisheries). If there is a fish kill incident, the Department of Agriculture (Fisheries) could prosecute under the Inland Fisheries Act. Licensing for discharges into watercourses has not yet been introduced, but is to be brought in within the next two years under a new Water Pollution Act.

Analysis of water pollution incidents in England and Wales

Industrial sources of pollution incidents are identified separately in England and Wales, enabling the construction industry's impact on water quality to be analysed in detail. Sources of water pollution are divided into sectors: sewage and water, industry, agriculture, transport, domestic/residential and "other". The industrial sector, which includes construction, caused 3600 water pollution incidents in England and Wales in 1998 (Figure 2.4), equivalent to 20 per cent of total incidents. Only the sewage and water and "other" sectors were larger contributors (24 and 28 per cent, respectively).

Within the industrial sector of England and Wales, the greatest identified contributor to pollution incidents in 1998 was the construction industry, with 17 per cent (625) of total incidents (Figure 2.5). There were three Category 1 pollution incidents (Figure 2.6), indicating that the majority of incidents from this sector are Category 2, 3 or 4.

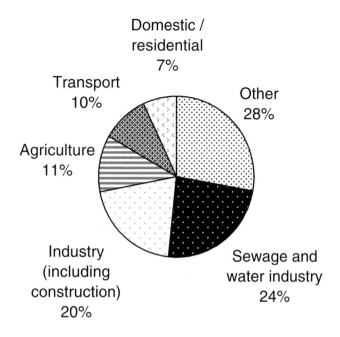

Figure 2.4   *Distribution of substantiated pollution incidents by source in England and Wales, 1998 (source: Environment Agency, 1999)*

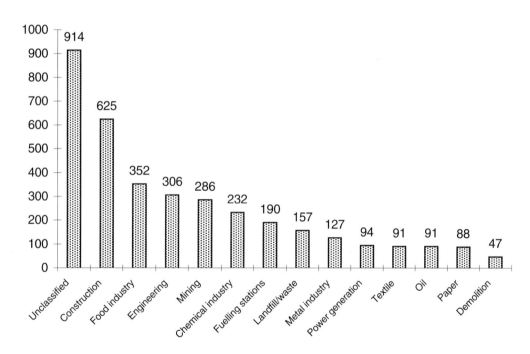

Figure 2.5   *Substantiated industrial pollution incidents by source, where classified, in England and Wales, 1998 (source: Environment Agency, 1999)*

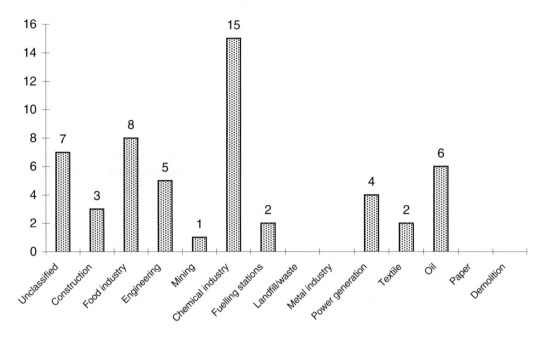

Figure 2.6   *Substantiated Category 1 industrial pollution incidents in England and Wales, 1998 (source: Environment Agency, 1999)*

The discharge of suspended solids and oil are the two most important areas of pollution linked to the construction industry. Hence the Environment Agency divides pollution incident data from the construction industry into suspended solids (see Case study 12), oil and other. The category of "other" could include chemical spills, and rubbish and sewage discharges. Each of these pollution types contributes only a few incidents in comparison to oil and suspended solids.

Case study 12 ☹   *Suspended sediments contaminate watercourse*

> A company was reclaiming a colliery using a contractor. Because of an inadequate maintenance programme, the wall of a slurry lagoon was breached and a discharge occurred to a river with excessively high levels of suspended solids. The two companies involved were charged under section 85(a) of WRA 1991 and pleaded guilty. Each company was fined £4000 with costs.
>
> *Source: Environ Law Mgmt 10(5) Sept–Oct 1998*

3 Legislative framework

3.1 INTRODUCTION

The law that governs the pollution of water is complex. There are three main reasons for this. First, it is divided into two parts, statute and common law, and both have a bearing on the matters under discussion in this book. Second, both elements have a long and complex history of precedent arising from cases and judgements made in the past, which sets the scene for contemporary actions and which continues to evolve. The third reason is the rapid pace of growth and change that has occurred in the law that relates to environmental matters over the past 10–15 years. This pace shows no sign of relenting; indeed, it appears to be accelerating.

Despite the complexity of this situation, almost everyone involved in construction must be aware, to some degree, of the responsibilities imposed upon them and of the consequences of any offence that might arise from their activities (see Case study 13). Section 3.2 is not intended to be a comprehensive guide to the law, or even to that part of the law relating to the pollution of water. There are many publications that cover this subject, some of which are listed in the references. This guidance document briefly defines the main elements of the statutory framework, highlights the regional variations in legislation across the UK, and points out the penalties that might be imposed when a successful prosecution is brought.

Case study 13 ⊗   *Neglect to repair equipment results in sediment discharge*

After public complaints, a site was visited and it was discovered that a sand-washing plant had been discharging its water directly into controlled water. The sediment load was so high that the discoloration was visible 5.5 km downstream. The company admitted that it had known of the discharge, which was the consequence of pump failure 10 days previously – a case of poor site management. The company pleaded guilty to a charge under section 85 of WRA 1991 and a fine of £8000 was imposed with costs.

Source: Environ Law Mgmt 9(5) Sep–Oct 1997

Section 3.3 provides a brief overview of the issues relating to occupational health and safety. For implementation of health and safety on site, reference should always be made to standard health and safety texts.

3.2 WATER LEGISLATION

3.2.1 European law

European legislation grows out of two basic sources. The first is the series of treaty provisions that provides a framework setting out the powers of the EU institutions and the decision-making procedures. This is referred to as "primary" law. Some of these provisions are directly effective in as much as they are followed by the national courts of each member state. Others are brought into effect within the legal system of each member state.

Within that framework lies the "secondary legislation" – a series of directives, decisions and regulations. Regulations have Community-wide effect and are binding on all member states. Directives are binding in achieving the required result, but leave each state to choose a method of implementation, usually through domestic law or regulation.

The aquatic environment is affected by several directives that have been enacted in the UK through various acts. Of these the most significant are:

- Groundwater Directive (80/68/EEC)
- Quality of surface water intended for the abstraction of drinking water (75/440/EEC)
- Quality of bathing water (76/160/EEC)
- Pollution caused by certain dangerous substances discharged into the aquatic environment (76/464/EEC)
- Quality of freshwaters needing protection or improvement to support fish life (78/659/EEC)
- Drinking Water Directive (80/778/EEC)
- Urban wastewater treatment (91/271/EEC).

3.2.2 Statutory law in England, Scotland and Wales

In England and Wales the law governing the pollution of water is enshrined principally in the Water Resources Act 1991 (WRA 1991), Part III of which is headed "Control of Pollution of Water Resources". This was amended by the Environment Act 1995 (EA 1995), which created the Environment Agency by combining the functions of the National River Authority (NRA), Her Majesty's Inspectorate of Pollution (HMIP) and the waste regulatory functions of the local authorities. The Environment Agency began operating on 1 April 1996 with a brief to protect, manage and enhance the environment (EA 1995, Part I, Sections 1–56).

In Scotland, the governing legislation is the Control of Pollution Act 1974 (COPA 1974) as amended by the Environment Act 1995 (EA 1995) and the Water Act 1989 (WA 1989). The regulatory authority is the Scottish Environment Protection Agency (SEPA), which was established by the EA 1995. On 1 April 1996, SEPA took over the role of the River Purification Authorities, Her Majesty's Industrial Pollution Inspectorate (HMIPI), the waste regulatory function of the district councils and others. In many respects SEPA's role and the extent of its powers differ from those of the Environment Agency.

In practice this legislation is applied by means of regulations, the most important of which are:

- The Anti-Pollution Works Regulations 1999
- The Groundwater Regulations 1998.

The Anti-Pollution Works Regulation 1999 came into force on 29 April 1999. It refers to works notices, which may be served under section 161 of the WRA 1991 (as amended by the EA 1995) to prevent or remedy pollution of controlled waters. The Environment Agency is thereby empowered to shift the emphasis from prosecution to prevention.

The Agency may serve a works notice on a person who has caused or knowingly permitted poisonous, noxious or polluting matter or any solid waste matter to be present at a place from which it is likely to enter controlled waters (both surface waters and groundwaters). The works notice will specify works or operations that the person must carry out to prevent that matter from entering the waters. In addition, a works notice will be used where clean-up is deemed necessary following a pollution incident, and will specify the works or operations required to restore the environment to its former state.

Failing to comply with a requirement of a works notice could lead to a fine of £20 000 and/or three months' imprisonment, and possibly legal action under section 85 of the WRA 1991 (s 85). The Agency may also carry out the necessary work and recover associated costs (these regulations do not apply in Scotland or Northern Ireland).

The Groundwater Regulations 1998 (Statutory Instrument 1998 no 2746) were introduced between 2 December 1998 and 1 April 1999 and relate to England, Wales and Scotland. They bring into force the Groundwater Directive (Council Directive 80/60/EEC) and they prevent the discharge of List I substances and limit the discharge of List II substances to groundwater. The controlled substances are listed below.

List I

The following substances, or groups of substances, are contained within List I:

- organohalogen compounds and substances that may form such compounds in the aquatic environment
- organophosphorus compounds
- organotin compounds
- substances that possess carcinogenic, mutagenic or teratogenic properties in or via the aquatic environment (including substances that have those properties which would otherwise be in List II)
- mercury and its compounds
- cadmium and its compounds
- mineral oils and hydrocarbons
- cyanides.

A substance may be excluded from List I if either the Environment Agency or SEPA considers it to be of low risk in terms of toxicity, persistence and bioaccumulation.

List II

A substance is in List II if it could have a harmful effect on groundwater and it belongs to one of the following families or groups of substances:

- the following metalloids and metals and their compounds:

zinc	tin
copper	barium
nickel	beryllium
chromium	boron
lead	uranium
selenium	vanadium
arsenic	cobalt
antimony	thallium
molybdenum	tellurium
titanium	silver

- biocides and their derivatives not appearing in List I

- substances that have a deleterious effect on the taste or odour of groundwater, and compounds liable to cause the formation of such substances in such water and to render it unfit for human consumption

- toxic or persistent organic compounds of silicon, and substances that may cause the formation of such compounds in water, excluding those which are biologically harmless or are rapidly converted in water into harmless substances

- inorganic compounds of phosphorus and elemental phosphorus

- fluorides

- ammonia and nitrites.

A substance is also in List II if:

- it belongs to one of the families or groups of substances set out in List 1

- it has been determined as inappropriate for List I by the environment regulator

- it has been determined by the Environment Agency or SEPA to be appropriate to List II having regard to toxicity, persistence and bioaccumulation.

Discharges, direct and indirect, of any List I substances are permitted unless, by prior investigation, provided by the applicant (defined in section 7 of the Regulations), it can be shown that all necessary technical precautions are observed. (An indirect discharge is one that reaches groundwater after percolation through the ground or subsoil.) A discharge may be approved if the prior investigation shows that:

> *"(a)... the groundwater is permanently unsuitable for other uses or the presence of that substance does not impede exploitation of ground resources and conditions are imposed which require that all technical precautions are observed to prevent that substance from reaching other aquatic systems or harming other ecosystems; or*

> *(b) the discharge is due to the re-injection into the same aquifer of water used for geothermal purposes, water pumped out of mines and quarries or water pumped out for civil engineering works."*

In a similar manner, authorisation for the direct or indirect discharge of List II substances shall not be granted unless, by prior investigation, it can be shown that "all necessary technical precautions are observed to prevent groundwater pollution".

An authorisation will be granted for a limited period and must be reviewed at least once every four years, at which time it may be renewed, amended or revoked. The regulations also give the environment regulator (Environment Agency or SEPA) the power to serve notice, in writing, to prohibit any activity that may directly pollute groundwater with a List I or II substance. Authorisations require surveillance of groundwater. Artificial recharges may be authorised on a case-by-case basis for the purpose of groundwater management, but only if there is no risk of polluting groundwater.

The new powers within the regulations introduce:

- a new requirement for authorisation for the disposal of List I and II substances in cases where a waste management licence under Part II of EPA 1990 is not already required

- a new procedure for prohibiting or regulating by notice other activities in or on land which pose an indirect threat to groundwater from List I or II substances.

There is an exclusion from the regulations where the environment regulator considers that the discharge contains List I or II substances "in a quantity and concentration so small as to obviate any present or future danger of deterioration in the quality of the receiving groundwater".

The List I and List II substances are also controlled in surface waters by the Dangerous Substances Directive (76/464/EEC) and its daughter directives. These have been converted into the following regulations for England, Wales and Scotland:

- The Surface Waters (Dangerous Substances) (Classification) Regulations 1997
- The Surface Waters (Dangerous Substances) (Classification) Regulations 1998
- The Surface Waters (Dangerous Substances) (Classification) (Scotland) Regulations 1990
- The Surface Waters (Dangerous Substances) (Classification) (Scotland) (no 2) Regulations 1998.

3.2.3   Statutory law in Northern Ireland

In Northern Ireland the legal system reflects that of England and Wales, but is distinct and different. Responsibility for regulating the aquatic environment is placed on the Department of the Environment (Northern Ireland) (DoE (NI)). This organisation is subdivided into the Water Executive, which is broadly responsible for water supply and sewerage services, and the Environment and Heritage Service, which deals with environmental regulation. The basis for this arrangement lies in the Water Act (Northern Ireland) 1972 (WA (NI) 1972) and the Water and Sewerage Services (Northern Ireland) Order 1973 (both of these have subsequent amendments). In addition WA (NI) 1972 is supported by a series of regulations and orders. The most significant of these are the Groundwater Regulations (Northern Ireland) 1998, which came into force during 1999. They prohibit the discharge of certain substances to the ground and aim to control the discharge of other substances and implement the Groundwater Directive 80/68/EEC for Northern Ireland. The same set of substances are controlled in surface waters by the Dangerous Substances Directive (76/464/EEC), which has been implemented in Northern Ireland as the Surface Waters (Dangerous Substances) Regulations (Northern Ireland) 1998.

3.2.4   Common law

The non-statutory law of the UK has evolved over the centuries by way of the judgements of High Court judges, a system referred known as "precedent". The law of tort, a branch of common law, deals with liabilities that occur between parties other than by formal arrangements such as contracts, leases and other agreements. Within this, the concept of private nuisance is of greatest relevance to water pollution. Private nuisance is the unlawful interference with a person's use or enjoyment of land or some right over it or in connection with it. Nuisance can arise from pollution of any of the environmental media, including controlled waters.

A person bringing a nuisance action must have an interest in the land affected. In the case of the pollution of a watercourse, the owners or occupiers of the land in contact with the watercourse will have rights of action. In the case of groundwater, any owner or occupier who can abstract from that source may sue. Nuisance can clearly go far beyond the boundary of the affected land and can open liability to a large number of parties with a wide range of interests.

Main criminal offences – England, Wales and Scotland

Criminal liabilities can arise under both common law and statute; the criminal law is not independent of civil law. A criminal prosecution for an act of pollution that causes damage to another person may become a preliminary to a much larger civil claim. However, this section will focus on statutory offences.

Controlled waters

This is defined in section 104 of the WRA 1991 for England and Wales, and in COPA 1974 as amended in Schedule 16 of EA 1995 for Scotland. In simple terms it covers:

- coastal and territorial waters, that is to say tidal waters and seawater within three nautical miles of the coastline
- inland freshwaters
- groundwaters.

Trade effluent or sewage effluent

Trade effluent is broadly defined to include any effluent discharged from premises used for carrying on any trade or industry, other than surface water or domestic sewage. Sewage effluent includes any effluent from the sewage disposal or sewerage works of a sewerage undertaker, but does not include surface water.

Poisonous, noxious or polluting matter

It is an offence to cause or knowingly permit any poisonous, noxious or polluting matter or any solid waste matter to enter any controlled waters (WRA 1991, s 85(1)). Proof of actual harm is not a prerequisite to liability for pollution (see Case study 14).

Case study 14 ⊗   *Construction site runoff pollutes watercourse*

In 1992, a defendant was found guilty in respect of construction site runoff that had polluted the River Tyne at Hexham. The contaminant had a significant biochemical oxygen demand (BOD). There was no evidence of any fish kill or other damage, but the quality of the watercourse had been reduced.

Cause or knowingly permit

This is an essential prerequisite under s 85 of the WRA 1991. "Causing" is an offence of strict liability. The prosecution must show intent or negligence on the part of the defendant. If the defendant was the effective cause of the pollution then they will be liable. If the pollution resulted from the act of another party then the defendant should not be found guilty.

"Knowingly permitting" is less clear cut in its definition. For example, if a source of pollution existed on land, and those pollutants migrated to nearby land or controlled waters, the owner or occupier of the land would not, at that moment, be knowingly permitting the discharge. However, having become aware of the migrating pollution they would have to take such measures as were within their powers to stop further pollution. Failure to do so would amount to knowingly permitting.

To ignore the obvious, or to refrain from inquiring because the truth is suspected and there is a desire not to have those suspicions confirmed, would also amount to knowingly permitting.

Where the pollution is the result of vandalism the question of knowingly permitting may depend upon whether or not the vandalism was foreseeable (see Case study 15).

Case study 15 ☹   *Inadequate measures allow vandals to cause pollution*

Vandals entered a site and broke pipes leading to tanks, allowing fuel to escape to a surface water drain leading to a river. A 6.5 km section was severely polluted, and it took a month to clean up. The company pleaded guilty to a charge under section 85 of WRA 1991. A fine of £7500 was imposed, with £1866 costs.

Source: Environ Law Mgmt 10(6) Nov–Dec 1998

The criminal offences

For activities in England and Wales the six principal water pollution offences are set out in section 85 of the WRA 1991. In Scotland, the same offences are set out in sections 31 and 32 of COPA 1974 as amended in Schedule 16 of EA 1995. They are:

- causing or knowingly permitting any poisonous, noxious, polluting matter or solid waste matter to enter controlled waters

- causing or knowingly permitting any matter other than trade effluent or sewage effluent to enter controlled waters from a drain or sewer in contravention of a prohibition under section 86

- causing or knowingly permitting any trade effluent to be discharged into any controlled waters or from land (through a pipe) outside the seaward limits of controlled waters

- causing or knowingly permitting any trade effluent or sewage effluent to be discharged, in contravention of a prohibition under section 86, from a building or from any fixed plant onto or into any land or into any waters of a lake or pond which are not inland freshwaters

- causing or knowingly permitting any matter whatever to enter any inland freshwater so as to tend (either directly or in combination with other matter) to impede the proper flow of the waters in a manner leading to, or likely to lead to, a substantial aggravation of pollution due to other causes, or the consequences of such pollution

- contravention of the conditions of a discharge consent.

All of the above relate to activities which are likely to be undertaken on construction sites, during initial construction work, routine maintenance or demolition. It is evident that almost any uncontrolled discharge to controlled waters has the potential to result in a criminal offence.

In addition, there is the offence of "statutory nuisance" which is defined in Part III of EPA 1990. This gives local authorities and certain members of the public the power to abate nuisance in a variety of environmental media. "Abatement notices" may be served or "abatement orders" obtained that not only require the abatement of the nuisance, but also allow the local authority to abate the pollution and recover their costs from a variety of persons, who may include the polluter and the owner or occupier of the premises concerned. Section 79 of EPA 1990 requires local authorities to inspect their areas for "statutory nuisances" and to respond to complaints of nuisance. It then has a duty to investigate any such complaint and, if it is satisfied that the nuisance exists, to serve an abatement notice requiring such work as may be necessary to abate the nuisance. The notice should be served on "the person responsible for the nuisance", but if that person cannot be found it can be served on the owner or occupier of the premises.

Ignorance of the law is not a defence, nor is ignorance of the facts. However, section 88(1) of WRA 1991, and section 30I(1) of COPA 1974 for Scotland, describe several defences. Any such defence will be supported if it can be shown that the incident is the result of an emergency, it has been notified to the relevant environment regulator and that all reasonable steps to remedy the situation were taken promptly.

3.2.6   Main criminal offences – Northern Ireland

In Northern Ireland the principal regulatory mechanisms are the discharge consent system set out in sections 7 and 8 of WA (NI) 1972. This regulates the discharge of trade and sewage effluents and any other polluting matter into coastal, inland and groundwaters, and the statutory water quality standards under sections 4B and 4C of the Act. In effect, discharges of effluent or any other polluting matter can only lawfully be made to inland, ground or coastal waters with the consent of the DoE (NI). To do so without such consent is a criminal offence. It is also a criminal offence to pollute such waters by the discharge or deposit of polluting matter. Section 5 of the Act defines this general offence as: "to cause or knowingly permit any deleterious matter to enter any waters"; where this is proven the offender is liable to summary conviction.

Where a breach of section 5 is likely to occur, or a repetition or continuation of an existing breach is likely, section 6(1) includes powers for serving notices that prohibit the proposed or actual use or permit the use or proposed use subject to certain conditions. Notices are served on either the owner of the land or the person using or proposing to use the land or water concerned. Enforcement is delegated by the Environment and Heritage Service to several agents, including the Foyle Fisheries Commission and the Fisheries Conservancy Board (FCB). The FCB takes samples under the River Water Quality Monitoring Program, investigates pollution incidents and prepares reports concerning potential prosecutions. It can also prosecute under the Sea Fisheries Regulations (NI) 1972, which are based on the Fisheries Act (1966).

The department is also empowered under section 13 of WA (NI) 1972 to serve notices prohibiting the deposition or discharge of any specified matter onto any land, into any waterway or into any underground strata that are specified in the notice. This is intended to prevent pollution before it occurs. Penalties for failing to comply with such a notice are the same as those for offences under sections 7 and 8 of the Act, set out in the following sections.

3.2.7   Penalties for water pollution

Penalties in England and Wales for breach of section 85 of the WRA 1991 are a maximum fine of £20 000 or imprisonment for up to three months, or both, upon summary conviction in the magistrates court. On conviction in the crown court, the penalty is an unlimited fine, or a term of imprisonment of up to of two years, or both (see Case study 16). In Scotland the fines are set at the same level for the same offences, as set out in COPA 1974 and amended by Schedule 16 of EA 1995.

Case study 16 ☹   *Oil pollution results in massive fine*

> In 1990 Shell was fined £1 million for the escape of 30 000 gallons of crude oil into a watercourse. This was on top of a payment of £1.4 million towards the costs of remedial operations.

Penalties for offences in Northern Ireland vary. If a prosecution is not considered to be warranted by the Environment Service, the polluter may still be required to pay the cost of clean-up and, if appropriate, compensation for any damage to fisheries. Where the

DoE (NI) pursues a prosecution, the penalties are the same as those in England and Wales. In addition the convicted person may be ordered by the court to "remedy or nullify" the breach of the law.

3.2.8   Individual and corporate liability

The law normally treats a company as a legal person that exists separately from its directors, officers, shareholders and employees. A company can commit crimes as a company and, except for imprisonment, it can incur the same penalties as a human criminal. A company can attract liabilities directly as a company and indirectly because of the actions of its employees.

Direct liability arises from the results of decisions of the "controllers" of the company – the directors and other superior officers who carry out the management function and speak and act as the company. Indirect (or vicarious) liability may result where the company has delegated the performance of a task to an employee without supervision. If the offence is one of strict liability (such as "causing" pollution) then vicarious liability will arise regardless of the delegation. In that case, the employer will remain liable even though the employee may have disregarded their instructions. (This is provided that the employee was acting in the course of their employment. The employer is not liable if the employee does something entirely outside the course of their employment.)

Individuals who are involved, even indirectly, in events leading up to or after a pollution incident may find themselves liable. Where the offence is due to the negligence, consent or connivance of a director, manager, company secretary or other similar officer of the company, then that person can be liable for that offence. This is provided for in several statutes, including EPA 1990 (s 157), WRA 1991 (s 217).

3.2.9   Discharge consents and licences

Before discharging water from a construction site a consent is required from the relevant environment regulator. The location, volume and composition of water discharged needs to comply with the consent (see Case study 17). The procedure involves the completion of an application form, submission of a location plan of the site showing the discharge locations and the likely nature and volume of the discharge, together with the necessary payment. Under the legislation the agencies have up to four months to determine the application, therefore sufficient time needs to be allowed before the start of works on site. In some circumstances – for example where particularly sensitive waters are involved – consent applications will have to be advertised to allow public consultation. In these cases, representations may be made, which might result in the granting of the consent being delayed beyond the four-month period. If the Secretary of State (First Minister, Scotland and Northern Ireland) calls in the consent, there is no time limit and the process can take a considerable length of time to resolve. In view of the fact that the discharge cannot legally begin until consent is granted, developers/contractors should ensure that applications are submitted with sufficient time to allow all necessary procedures to take place to avoid construction being delayed.

Where a consent exists and is being contravened or is likely to be contravened, the Environment Agency may serve an enforcement notice specifying the steps that must be taken to remedy the situation and the period within which those steps must be taken.

If the project requires dewatering of the ground and associated recharge, the recharge may require a discharge consent. Special care must be taken where the ground may be contaminated, as dewatering could result in the mobilisation of contaminated groundwaters.

When disposing of List I and II substances into or onto land, the discharger should apply for an authorisation under the Groundwater Regulations (see Section 3.2.2). This may apply to the discharge of contaminated water from a brownfield site where the discharge is made onto or into land. Under normal circumstances, a consent would be considered under the WRA 1991 by the environment regulator. Charges would be levied for such an application plus a subsistence fee for maintenance of the authorisation.

Case study 1 ☹   *Discharge without consent results in prosecution*

> Following public complaint, orange pollution in a river was traced to the defendant's site. A pump was found to be directing dirty water into the river rather than into settlement lagoons. The company was charged under section 85(1) of WRA 1991 and pleaded guilty. A fine of £4000 was imposed with costs.
>
> *Source: Environ Law Mgmt 10(6) Nov–Dec 1998*

In Northern Ireland, discharge consents must be obtained from the DoE (NI). Different systems exist for discharges to sewers and for discharge to inland, coastal and ground-waters (waterway or underground strata). The application must contain information on the nature of the discharge. There may be a need to publish notices of the application in specified newspapers. DoE (NI) grants discharge consents subject to such conditions as it thinks fit, and it maintains a register of consents and conditions currently in force, which is open to public inspection.

The discharge consent typically contains limits for pH, suspended solids and oils. On occasions there may be a requirement for temperature and volume to be consented, and a flow measurement device, such as a v-notch weir, may need to be incorporated into the works at the outfall. The environment regulator will apply annual charges for the consented discharge.

3.2.10   How to apply for a consent

Northern Ireland

Abstractions – there is no licensing system for abstraction in Northern Ireland; consequently, there are no abstraction licences.

Boreholes – there is no licensing system for abstraction in Northern Ireland; consequently, there are no borehole licences.

Working near watercourses – there is no formal application form for working near watercourses, although consent is required under the Drainage NI Order 1973. The applicant must submit a written proposal and plans/drawings to DARD Rivers Service (under the Drainage Northern Ireland Order 1973). There is no charge for the administration of these consents. The legislation gives DARD up to three months to reply. Consent generally lasts indefinitely, although specific projects may have time limits attached if it is known that circumstances may change. It is unlikely that a consent for constructing a temporary structure within a watercourse would be refused, although conditions may be attached to the consent to impose liability for damage caused.

Land drainage – there is no legislation covering land drainage in Northern Ireland.

Discharges – a consent is required to discharge sewage and trade effluents and other discharges such as cooling waters. Within the consent upper or lower limits may be set for parameters which may include pH, BOD, suspended solids, temperature and oil levels. An application form for a discharge consent in Northern Ireland is presented in Appendix A1. There is no application fee for a discharge consent in Northern Ireland, but the applicant is required to pay for the application to be advertised in the press.

Once the Environment and Heritage Service receives an application, it generally responds within four months. The EHS may apply for an extension if there are unresolved issues associated with the application. If the applicant refuses to allow the extension, then a decision must be made at that point, and the application may be refused. Once granted, the discharge consent lasts indefinitely while the discharge continues. If the discharge ceases for a period of three years, the consent ceases to be valid. If the consent is refused, under the Water Act (NI) 1972, the applicant can appeal to the independent body, the Water Appeals Commission. (A new order is likely to be brought in to replace the current Water Act in the near future, but it is likely to retain the majority of features of the current Act.) The applicant must submit an appeal in writing within 28 days of receiving the decision from the EHS. The Water Appeals Commission will request a submission from the EHS and will set a date for a hearing. At this hearing the Commission will recommend that the decision be upheld or quashed.

England and Wales

Abstractions – an application for an abstraction licence has to be completed for new abstractions, and to vary an existing abstraction licence. Appendix A2 reproduces an application form for a licence to abstract water in England and Wales. The licence covers abstraction from sources that include surface waters and underground strata (for example from boreholes). Except when the abstraction is less than 20 m^3/day, the application must generally be published by means of press advertising and making the application available for public inspection. The application must include a map, with appropriate areas highlighted and referenced in the text of application. The Environment Agency charges £110 (October 1999) for each abstraction application. Each licence-holder is also subject to an annual charge, based on calculation of such factors as licensed volume abstracted, season, source and loss. The applicant and/or the Environment Agency specify the duration of the licence. The EA decides on an abstraction application within three months of receiving it. If an indefinite licence is granted this will also expire on a specified date.

If the applicant is dissatisfied with the EA's decision, or if the Agency does not respond within the specified time, the applicant can appeal to the Secretary of State (DETR). The appeal must be made within 28 days of the EA's decision, or the date by which it should have responded. The applicant must inform the Environment Agency of the decision to appeal. The Secretary of State may instigate a local inquiry and call the applicant and the Agency to appear before them, or make a decision without using these methods. The decision of the Secretary of State is final.

Land drainage – under WRA 1991 and relevant byelaws, a land drainage consent is required from the Environment Agency if works are to be carried out in, over, under or near a watercourse or flood defence. The aim is to ensure that works do not endanger life or property by increasing the risk of flooding or cause harm to the water environment. Appendix A3 gives an example of the application form to apply for a land drainage consent in England and Wales.

When submitting plans and drawings with the application, three copies of all relevant drawings are required. These should include a location plan, site plan, detailed drawings and sketches. The fee charged by the Environment Agency to cover the costs of examining the proposals is £50 (as of October 1999) per application. Upon receipt of an application, the Environment Agency has two months in which to grant or refuse consent. The application is deemed to have been granted if it is neither granted nor refused within the two-month period.

If the consent is withheld, or if the applicant is of the opinion that conditions attached to the consent are unreasonable, the issue may be referred to an arbitrator appointed by agreement between the applicant and the Agency. If the parties do not reach agreement, the president of the Institution of Civil Engineers conducts the arbitration. If the applicant and the Environment Agency do not agree to arbitration, the issue is referred to, and determined by, the Secretary of State.

Discharges – a discharge consent is required to discharge sewage effluent, trade effluent or other matter. Within the consent upper or lower limits may be set for parameters including pH, BOD, suspended solids, temperature and oil levels. An example of the application form to apply for a new consent or a variation to a discharge consent is presented in Appendix A4.

A fee is charged for each consent application, and depends on the type of effluent discharged. The application fee for discharges of sewage effluent (less than 5 m^3/day), cooling water (10 m^3/day) and uncontaminated water is £88 (as of October 1999). In all other cases, the fee for each discharge, including site runoff, is £617 (October 1999). A further annual charge may also be payable from the date of coming into force of any consent issued. The applicant will also be required to pay for the discharge application to be advertised in a local newspaper and in the *London Gazette*, and a charge of £50 (October 1999) will be made for the advertising administration costs. The Environment Agency also requires that the application be submitted with a site plan indicating the location of the premises, the discharge and sampling points, and any other information requested in the application form. A decision will be made on the application within four months. If no response is received from the Agency by the end of this period, the application can be assumed to have been refused. However, if a problem with the application arises, the Agency would probably contact the applicant within the four-month period.

If the Environment Agency refuses, revokes or attaches conditions to a discharge consent, then the applicant may make an appeal to the Secretary of State. If the Secretary of State considers that the decision of the Environment Agency should be modified or reversed, directions to that effect will be issued to the Agency.

Scotland

Abstraction – abstraction licences are issued for one-year periods and therefore have to be renewed annually. Appendix A5 presents an example of an application form to apply for a consent to abstract water in Scotland. A fee of £50 is required for each application for a licence to abstract (October 1999). The closing date for receipt of applications for the licence period 1 January–31 December 2000 was 15 September 1999, with SEPA to inform the applicant of the decision by 10 November 1999. It is understood that similar dates will be set by SEPA every year. If SEPA fails to inform the applicant of the decision by the specified date then a licence will be granted unconditionally.

Land drainage – there is no procedure in Scotland for obtaining land drainage consents.

Working near a watercourse – there is no procedure in Scotland for obtaining land drainage consents.

Discharges – a consent is required from SEPA for discharges released into surface waters. Within the consent upper or lower limits may be set for parameters including pH, BOD, suspended solids, temperature and oil levels. An example of the application form to apply for a consent to discharge in Scotland is provided in Appendix A6.

A fee is charged for each licence application. The standard application charge is £546 (October 1999) and the reduced application charge is £78 (October 1999). The reduced application charge applies where the discharge contains:

- effluent which, before treatment, contains a BOD loading of 900 g/day or less and does not contain toxic, persistent or other potentially harmful substances

- effluent from cooling or heat exchange processes where the proposed volume to be discharged is 10 m³ or less per day.

The applicant is also required to pay for the discharge application to be advertised in a local newspaper and the *Edinburgh Gazette*.

The application must include a map showing the location of the site, a drainage layout plan, the design and performance of effluent treatment plant, the design of the outlet and sampling chamber, and details of any other outlet from the site. The application can be assumed to have been refused if SEPA does not notify the applicant of a decision within four months.

3.2.11 Planning conditions

The number and type of planning conditions relating to the construction phase of a development may vary between local authorities (LAs), with some conditions detailed and quite prescriptive and others more general. The issues generally covered by planning conditions are given below.

Road contamination

The planning conditions may describe the plant which must be installed to prevent mud and debris being deposited on external roads. This might read: "Measures shall be taken to ensure that no mud or other loose material is deposited on the public highway. If necessary wheel-cleaning equipment shall be installed, used and maintained." The instructions may provide significantly more detail, describing the type of wheel-wash facility to be installed, such as a pond or spray type.

The conditions may include instructions to ensure that the access between the wheel-wash and the public road is surfaced with concrete, that water bowsers and uncontaminated water are available to reduce dust pollution in dry periods and that vehicles transporting loose materials off site are securely sheeted to prevent spillage onto roads.

Fuel and chemical storage

Planning conditions relating to storage of fuel, oils and chemicals on site may describe, for example, that they "be sited on impervious bases and surrounded by impervious bund walls. The volume of the bunded compound shall be at least equivalent to the capacity of the tank or tanks plus 10 per cent." Other planning conditions may state that fuel and chemical storage "be sited and bunded in a manner so as to retain any spillage to the satisfaction of the Environment Agency" (or SEPA or EHS). Further information on constructing bunds can be found in the joint CIRIA and EA guideline, *Concrete bunds for oil storage tanks*. More detail, suitable for large or complex construction, can be found in *Construction of bunds for oil storage tanks* (CIRIA R163, 1997a). Some of the consequences of inadequate bunding are described in Case study 18.

Case study 18 ⊗   *Inadequate earth bund results in fish kill*

> A company injected brewery waste into a field adjacent to a stream entering a nature reserve. It placed an earth dam in the way, but effluent escaped into the water and fish were killed. The company was charged under section 85(1) of WRA 1991. The company pleaded guilty and was fined £3000, with £4919 clean-up costs.
>
> *Source: Environ Law Mgmt 10(3) May–Jun 1998*

Surface water drainage

Planning conditions relating to the disposal of surface water are typically concerned with ensuring that drainage systems provided are adequate for the quantity and type of water draining from the site, during both the construction and operational phases. The function of these conditions is to prevent pollution of watercourses close to the site. The conditions may include descriptions of the type or standard of gullies or oil interceptors to be included within the drainage system. For example: "The surface water drainage system serving any access roads shall be provided with trapped gullies to British Standard BS5911 (1982) or to any higher standard as required by the Environment Agency". Other conditions may specifically stipulate separate disposal of surface water drainage from car parks, roads and roofs. For example: "all surface water drainage from parking areas and hardstandings shall be passed through trapped gullies and an oil interceptor … Roof water shall not pass through the interceptor (to prevent pollution of the water environment)."

"Model" planning conditions

The document *Planning for quality in minerals and waste development control* (CPO Society, 1995) contains recommended "model" planning conditions. Some of these, although designed for mineral extraction and waste disposal sites, are applicable to construction sites, and may be utilised by local planning authorities.

> **Examples of model conditions**
>
> (i)   No development hereby permitted shall be brought into use unless and until a detailed scheme to accommodate surface water runoff, including that of adjacent areas dependent on the area for their own drainage, has been submitted to and approved in writing by the Waste Planning Authority. No development shall take place except in accordance with the approved scheme and plan(s)
>
> or
>
> (ii)   a detailed scheme for the drainage and disposal of surface water shall be submitted to the waste planning authority within (*xx*) months of the date of this permission. On approval by the Waste Planning Authority the scheme shall be implemented within (*yy*) months of the date of approval.
>
> *Reason: to ensure adequate drainage of the site.*

(iii) Measures shall be taken for the overall drainage of the site/(and the prevention of pollution by leachate), in accordance with (the details in approved plan no. *xx*)/(a scheme which shall have been submitted to and approved in writing by the Waste Planning Authority and thereafter fully implemented)

or

(iv) there shall be no discharge of trade effluent, sewage effluent or contaminated water from the site into any Environment Agency "controlled waters" viz soakaways, ditches, watercourses, ponds or lakes.

Reason: to safeguard water quality.

(v) No surface water from the site shall be discharged into any ditch, watercourse drain or area of surface water unless it has first passed through a suitably sized oil interceptor.

Reason: to prevent pollution of receiving waters (where this is not covered by controls under the Environmental Protection Act).

Drainage condition where the site adjoins areas of nature conservation importance

Exceptionally, an application may come forward which is acceptable but where there are very particular requirements to safeguard adjacent land – to a degree beyond the normal concerns for pollution control exercised by the Environment Agency, such as where nature conservation interests require a particular concern over runoff. An example of such a condition used in practice is as follows.

The development hereby permitted shall not be commenced until details of the following works have been submitted to and approved in writing by the Waste Planning Authority:

(a) details of works proposed to control surface water within and adjacent to the site

(b) control, management and monitoring measures to safeguard the adjacent SSSI, including measures for monitoring and controlling:

   (i) groundwater levels and quality (in relation to dewatering and its land-use implications)
   (ii) surface water levels in and adjoining the landfill area, including groundwater discharge areas and surface water drains, to safeguard against siltation or erosion affecting the heathland. These procedures shall include trigger levels and contingency measures to be put into effect in the event that these levels are exceeded.

Reason: in the interests of amenity and to protect (xx).

Dust

(i) No development shall be commenced until a scheme to minimise the emission of dust from the development hereby authorised (including measures to monitor emissions) has been submitted to and approved in writing by the Water Planning Authority. Such a scheme shall include (the water spraying of access and haul roads to suppress dust in periods of prolonged dry weather), and shall be implemented in full and the suppression equipment thereafter maintained in accordance with the manufacturer's instructions for the duration of the permission, unless with the prior written approval of the Waste Planning Authority of a variation. During adverse weather conditions (which will need to be defined as part of the conditions – ie based on wind direction and wind speed), operations close to affected properties shall cease, to minimise the possibility of dust nuisance.

Reason: to protect the amenities of local residents.

Groundwater and watercourses – model conditions

(i)   Any oil, fuel, lubrication and other potential pollutants shall be handled on the site in such a manner as to prevent pollution of any watercourse or aquifer. For any liquid other than water, this shall include storage in suitable tanks and containers which shall be housed in an area surrounded by bund walls of sufficient height and construction so as to contain 110 per cent of the total contents of all containers and associated pipework. The floor and walls of the bunded areas shall be impervious to both water and oil. The pipes should vent downwards into the bund.

Reason: to minimise the risk of pollution of watercourses and aquifers.

(ii) No extraction tipping or temporary storage of materials shall take place within (*xx* m) of any watercourse. Under no circumstances shall tipped material enter any watercourse or culvert.

Reason: to minimise the risk of pollution of watercourses and aquifers.

(iii) Prior to commencement of extraction from the site, details of the location and arrangements for the monitoring of groundwater levels for the duration of the working shall be submitted for approval by the relevant authority and thereafter implemented as approved.

Reason: to assess the risk of effects arising from changes in groundwater levels (relate to particular circumstances of the application or as requested by the environment regulator).

(iv) There shall be no working below … AOD.

Reason: to minimise the risk of groundwater pollution (relate to particular circumstance of the application or as requested by the environment regulator), to cater for different geological or hydrogeological conditions below the working level and to minimise the effect on local groundwater resources.

(From CPO Society, 1995)

3.3 HEALTH AND SAFETY LEGISLATION

3.3.1 Introduction

Most work activities associated with the control of water pollution impose occupational health and safety duties on the management. It is not intended in this section to detail all applicable health and safety legislation relating to the protection of the workforce. This can be found in other publications. However, an overview of the main requirements is given and the key legislation is listed below:

- Health and Safety at Work Act 1974, Chapter 37
- Management of Health and Safety at Work 1992, SI no 2051
- Management of Health and Safety at Work (amendments) 1994, SI no 2865
- Control of Substances Hazardous to Health Regulations 1998, SI no 43**
- Control of Major Accident Regulations 1999, SI no 743
- Construction, Design and Management Regulations 1994, SI no 3140
- Construction (Health and Safety, Welfare) Regulations 1996, SI no 1592
- The control of Pollution (Special Waste) Regulations 1980, SI no 1709.

Modern health and safety legislation is based upon the concept that managers should identify the hazards faced by those they put to work. Then, by developing safe systems of work, managers should eliminate or minimise those risks to the lowest reasonably practicable level. Key to this approach, which is embedded in much of the legislation, is the process of "risk assessment"

3.3.2 Risk assessment

The Health and Safety at Work Act 1974 and the regulations made under the Act provide a framework for the management of health and safety, particularly the provisions of the Management of Health and Safety At Work Regulations 1992. The latter requires that a "suitable and sufficient assessment of health and safety risks shall be made to enable appropriate control measures to be put into place". A suitable and sufficient assessment is one that:

- correctly identifies any significant risks that are foreseeable

- enables the assessor to identify and prioritise what actions are needed to eliminate or minimise the risk

- covers what the employer can reasonably and practicably be expected to know about the risks associated with his or her undertaking.

The process of planning for safety can be considered as having six stages.

1. Hazard identification – identifying potential causes of harm.

2. Risk assessment – assessing the risk that may arise from the hazards.

3. Risk control – deciding on suitable measures to eliminate or control the risk.

4. Implementing and maintaining control measures – implementing standards and ensuring they are effective.

5. Monitoring and reviewing the activity and assessment to ensure that assumptions made were valid and to identify further improvements that can be made.

6. Record-keeping – employers employing five or more staff must record their risk assessments in writing. Risk assessments should be retained for archiving with other safety documentation.

Definitions of the key terms are given below.

Hazard – a property, situation or substance with potential to cause harm.

Risk – the combination of the probability of that potential hazard being realised; the severity of the outcome if it is and the number of people exposed to the hazard.

Risk assessment – "a carefully considered judgement" requiring an evaluation of the risk that may arise from the hazards identified, combination of the various factors contributing to the risk and evaluation of their significance.

Risk control – the definition of the measures necessary to control the risk, coupled with their implementation; the management of the risk. The risk management process must include the arrangements for monitoring the effectiveness of the control measures together with their review to ensure continuing relevance.

Hierarchy of controls

When risks have been assessed, decisions can be made about control measures. These must always take into account any relevant legal requirements establishing minimum levels of risk prevention or control. Decisions about the reliability or suitability of control measures should be guided by the hierarchy of controls set out below.

1. Avoid risks.

2. Combat risks at source.

3. Adapt the work to the individual.

4. Use up-to-date control measures.

5. Develop a coherent policy and approach.

6. Give priority to "collective" rather than individual protective measures.

7. Train and educate the workforce.

In general, the employer of the person carrying out the work is responsible for assessing the risk and developing a safe system of work. Where the person or organisation is working under a subcontract, their activities must be considered as part of the undertaking. The project/site manager must be satisfied that a suitable and sufficient risk assessment has been made and a safe system of work developed. The significant risks identified during the assessment process and the safe system of work developed should be recorded in writing.

Where the employer acts as principal contractor for the project they also have a duty to obtain risk assessments and method statements from all the contractors working on the project and to ensure that the activities of each contractor are properly co-ordinated.

In addition to the requirement for a general assessment of risks contained in the Management of Health and Safety at Work Regulations (1992), several other regulations (Young Persons, COSHH, Noise at Work, Manual Handling, Personal Protective Equipment, etc) call for risk assessments to be carried out with regard to specific risk areas.

The HSC Approved Code of Practice (ACOP) also indicates that, for construction activities, numeric systems for calculating risk are not required and a simple categorisation of high, medium and low should suffice.

The onus must always be to do more rather than less to minimise the risk. The Health and Safety at Work Act (1974) requires employers to prevent their employees and others affected by their business from being exposed to risk so far as is reasonably practicable.

An action can only be considered as impracticable if the risk of injury or illness is low and the cost of preventing exposure to that risk disproportionately high by a significant margin.

Review of risk assessments

Risk assessment should not be seen as a one-off process. Assessments must be kept under review and revised if there is any substantive change in the system of work, work environment or personnel.

The fact that a review has taken place should be recorded, even if no changes to the assessment of safe system of work were deemed necessary. Where changes are made to either the safe system of work or the assessment, they must be communicated as per the issue it replaces.

Communication of risk assessments

Risk assessments, or the relevant parts thereof, must be adequately communicated, in a comprehensible manner, to those likely to be affected by the work activity. This will include:

- contractors or employers whose employees may be affected by the works covered by the assessment
- employees and supervisors who will be expected to carry out the activity covered by the assessment
- other employees working in the vicinity of the activity.

The precise arrangements made on each site for communicating information contained in risk assessments and method statements should be set out in the construction phase Health and Safety Plan as required by CDM.

3.3.3   Construction (Design & Management) Regulations 1994 (CDM)

The Construction (Design and Management) Regulations 1994 (CDM) incorporate the European Union Directive on health and safety requirements at temporary or mobile construction sites (92/57/EEC) into UK legislation. They establish a framework for managing the health and safety aspects of construction projects throughout the design and construction phases. They also require that designers give adequate consideration to how structures they design can be constructed, cleaned, maintained, and ultimately demolished, safely and with regard to the health of those doing the work.

The regulations describe in great detail criminal law duties regarding health and safety imposed on clients and designers. They call for the designer to appoint a co-ordinator (the planning supervisor). The planning supervisor's duties include co-ordinating the work of designers with respect to construction health and safety and ensuring that information is provided for use by those constructing the project, and by the client.

Designers are charged with reducing the risk faced by those constructing their designs by eliminating hazards during the design process wherever reasonably practicable, as well as passing on relevant information about residual hazards in their design.

The regulations call for the appointment of a construction phase co-ordinator (the principal contractor), who is responsible for establishing measures for the management of health and safety of all aspects of the "construction works" on the project.

Contractors and the self-employed are also given duties to co-operate with others in executing their duties and fulfilling their own legal responsibilities under other legislation.

The CDM Regulations change many of the definitions in previous legislation and also introduce new definitions. Full details of these definitions can be found in the regulations or in the approved code of practice (ACOP) that accompanies them.

The regulations do not apply to every construction project. For example, if the local authority is the enforcing authority then none of the regulations apply. Depending on the nature of the work, the client and the scale of the project, particular regulations will or will not apply. Refer to the HSC guide *Designing for health and safety in construction* (1995) for a detailed breakdown.

3.3.4 Control of Substances Hazardous to Health (COSHH)

Where oils and chemicals or other potentially hazardous substances are brought onto site, consideration should be given to the requirements of the COSHH Regulations during their storage, transportation and use. These regulations describe the measures that have to be taken to control the exposure of employees and others to substances hazardous to their health. EH40, a Health and Safety Executive Guidance Note updated annually, contains maximum exposure limits and occupational exposure standards for numerous substances designated as hazardous to health

The following abbreviations are used in health and safety documentation:

- **MEL** – maximum exposure limit;
- **OES** – occupational exposure standard
- **MSDS** – manufacturer's safety data sheet.

Employers and managers should ensure that suitable training is given to those required to assess risks arising from substances hazardous to health likely to be encountered in the workplace.

So far as is possible, the identification of substances likely to be hazardous to health will take place at the planning stage. Those substances that are likely to be outside the experience of a competent contractor or pose significant risk should be mentioned in the health and safety plan. Consideration must be given not only to substances received from manufacturers and outside suppliers but also to substances likely to be encountered or created, such as dust, contaminated land or micro-organisms likely to cause disease.

Certain hazardous substances, like lead and asbestos, are subject to specific regulations. Where such substances are identified, an assessment of the risk to health must be made in line with COSHH. Suitable control measures and, where necessary, health surveillance will then need to be planned and carried out.

The COSHH written assessment should consist of the following parts:

- identification of the substances to be assessed
- an assessment of the risks to health
- an outline of the necessary measures to eliminate or reduce the risks and ensure that exposure of employees and others to the substances is kept to the lowest reasonably practicable level, below any relevant MEL and within any relevant OES
- the type(s) of control measures, if any, needed to eliminate or reduce the hazard to health together with a record of their effectiveness and maintenance
- the need or otherwise for environmental monitoring and health surveillance
- identification of individuals or groups of individuals needing information, instruction, training and supervision in the use of the listed substances
- an MSDS file together with any other information used by the assessors in making the various risk assessments, such as environmental monitoring results
- review dates at appropriate intervals.

It should be the responsibility of the person placing an order to ensure that MSDS in respect of substances purchased for site use are received and have been passed to the relevant site manager.

All subcontractors should be required to produce COSHH assessments for their activities before starting work. Upon the completion of assessments, they should communicate relevant information to those carrying out and supervising the works. A full copy of the assessment should be held on file for future reference. Site managers should ensure that there is a free exchange of information between their contractors with regard to any relevant COSHH assessments and the control measures needed to avoid risks to health.

No employee or operative should be required to use or be exposed to any of the substances listed in the assessments unless sufficient information and instruction has been provided to enable the work to be carried out without risk to health. Such information can be given by individual induction or by means of a toolbox safety talk. The purpose of a toolbox talk is to communicate the safe system of work to employees, and it should be utilised in as much job safety training as possible, both formal (site training room) and informal (on-the-job contract sessions). From a practical viewpoint, toolbox talks should be listed on cards which should be (a) posted in the area in which the job is to be undertaken, (b) issued to all relevant employees individually, and (c) referred to and explained in all related training sessions.

Written records of COSHH induction training and toolbox talks should be kept. Copies of any environmental monitoring records are best held with the COSHH assessments. Records of health surveillance and/or biological monitoring should also be kept.

3.3.5 The Control of Major Accidents (COMA)

The Control of Major Accident Regulations 1999, SI no 743 (COMA), came into force on 1 April 1999. COMA imposes a general duty on every operator (person in control of operation of an establishment or installation) to prepare and keep a document setting out policy for preventing major accidents (major accident prevention policy document). The policy must be designed and formulated to guarantee a high level of protection for persons and the environment by appropriate competent persons, structures and management systems.

3.3.6 Communication

Good communication is an essential part of ensuring that not only are the goals for achievement made known to all those involved, but also that the timing, reasons and methods are fully understood so they are followed in producing the required quality of product or efficiency of service. Communications should be made in terms that can be understood by the recipients so that decisions can be clearly conveyed, confusion is prevented and any procedures properly followed.

Care must be taken to ensure that communication does not "leapfrog" levels of organisation. To get the maximum benefit from communications, all relevant levels in the organisation should be included, whether written (news sheets, notice board) or verbal (toolbox talks, presentations etc) means are used. Good communications will reduce conflict and improve workplace relations, but they are not the only means nor are they a complete solution. Set out below are key times for the communication of information. Note this is not a definitive list and each contractor and consultant should develop methods and procedures for the appropriate communication of information.

- client to designer – the project objectives and constraints
- consultant to contractor – specification/tender, tender interviews, pre-contract meetings and regular progress meetings
- contractor to site staff and other subcontractors – site inductions, toolbox talks and regular site progress meetings.

3.3.7   Water-related health and safety issues

This section is intended to be a general overview of water-related health and safety issues and is not intended to be a definitive list. The consultant and contractor should carry out the appropriate risk assessment and comply with the CDM, COSHH and COMA regulations for each and every site.

1. Persons working over water run the risk, if control measures are not in place, of falling in and drowning. Rescue can be hampered if the water is fast-flowing or if appropriate life-saving equipment is not readily available. The temperature of the water and especially the presence of ice increase the danger.

2. Biohazards can be present in water although they are not visible, eg Weil's disease (see Section 3.3.8). Sewerage causes bacterial viruses, which are invisible to the naked eye. Chemicals can also be present in the water and can cause skin infections, eye irritations and other harmful effects if ingested (see Section 3.3.9).

3. When excavations become filled with water, the depth will not be known as the water will be discoloured. It is important that good edge protection and signage is provided. An appropriate means of escape must be provided, such as a ladder.

4. Standing surface water can cause persons to slip and fall and vehicles to skid. Below 0° C, icy conditions occur and can worsen conditions on access routes.

5. The operation of plant and machinery can be disrupted because of frozen or burst pipes. This can lead to working areas being affected, causing slip hazards, especially when the water mixes with existing chemicals that have been spilt. This contaminated water may then run off into controlled watercourses, leading to possible legal action by the environment regulators.

6. Water stored in tanks or temporary bunded reservoirs can escape if not correctly controlled. This can case a hazard to people and plant if caught in the line of the breach. Escaped water can run into storage areas and could collect contaminated materials; this water would then have to be collected or the contaminated ground treated as part of a clean-up operation.

3.3.8   Waterborne health hazards

The most significant waterborne disease to affect humans in the UK that is not contracted by drinking infected water is leptospirosis. This is a bacterial infection transmitted to humans by bodily contact with infected water. The bacteria can enter the body through cuts and scratches and through the lining of the mouth, throat and eyes after contact with infected water. There are two forms of this disease:

- Weil's disease – a serious and sometimes fatal infection that is transmitted to humans by contact with urine from infected rats (see Site procedure 9)

- Hardjo leptospirosis, which is transmitted from cattle to humans.

The early symptoms of leptospirosis are a flu-like illness with a persistent and severe headache. The disease can rapidly bring about jaundice, kidney failure and death if not treated early with antibiotics. People undertaking work in and around water should be issued with a card detailing the risk of exposure to this disease that they can present to their doctor in the event of the above symptoms occurring.

The risk of contracting the disease can be reduced by wearing protective clothing when in contact with water, and covering all cuts and broken skin with waterproof plasters. Correct storage and disposal of organic waste can prevent rats multiplying on site. Site procedure 9 gives an example of the safety measures that should be conveyed to staff who are at risk of contracting leptospirosis.

Another health hazard associated with water is from toxins produced by blue-green algae. These toxins may be produced in high enough concentrations to affect humans, particularly if the algae accumulate to form a scum on the water surface. Symptoms of poisoning by blue-green algal toxins can range from asthma, hayfever and conjunctivitis if the toxin comes into contact with the skin, to abdominal pain, vomiting, diarrhoea and pneumonia if the toxin is swallowed.

3.3.9   Working with pesticides and herbicides

The use of pesticides and herbicides on site may be necessary when undertaking site clearance procedures. The use of pesticides is controlled by Part III of the Food and Environment Protection Act (FEPA 1985), the Control of Pesticides Regulations 1986 (COPR), and the Control of Substances Hazardous to Health (COSHH 1988) regulations made under the Health and Safety at Work Act 1974.

There may be inherent health hazards associated with use of even approved pesticides and herbicides. It is essential, therefore, that appropriate assessments are made before use, the pesticides are used and stored correctly by properly qualified operatives, and that suitable personal protective clothing is worn. A code of practice on the safe use of pesticides on farms has been produced by the Ministry of Agriculture, Fisheries and Food (MAFF and HSC, 1990). This document includes much useful information on the safe storage, use and disposal of pesticides, regardless of whether they are to be used on farms, construction sites or in any other situation. It also gives details of COSSH assessments of pesticide usage, the training necessary to use pesticides, and monitoring of exposure to pesticides. Another document produced by the Ministry of Agriculture, Fisheries and Food (MAFF, 1991) provides details regarding the correct use of herbicides and pesticides with regard to watercourses and groundwater, storage, application and disposal.

4 Construction contracts

4.1 INTRODUCTION

Most construction work is performed under contract. The contract sets out the rights and duties of the parties. Sometimes the contract will have detailed written terms; sometimes it will simply be a short letter or even a "gentleman's agreement". Regardless of the form of contract, those involved are usually in agreement that a contract exists. Problems are usually based on the interpretation of the contract and the balance of risk and responsibility. This guidance is relevant to all types of contract – traditional, design-and-build, design-build-finance-operate (DBFO) and partnering.

Formal construction contracts generally have a standard form of conditions that can be amended to suit, along with various other documents. These other documents may be standard or unique to the project and are likely to include the scope of the work, setting out details, standards of materials and workmanship required, and methods of valuation and payment. Other documents frequently produced include method statements and programmes, although these may or may not have formal contractual status.

The contract between the parties involved in a construction project is the most effective vehicle for setting out specific requirements for implementing the work and defining the responsibilities of the various parties. The contract forms reviewed are not exhaustive but they place the burden of responsibility for dealing with the environmental impact of any work, be it newbuild, maintenance or demolition, with the contractor. This may be explicit or implicit. There may be specific reference to environmental matters, or merely a requirement to "meet all statutory and regulatory requirements".

4.1.1 Design-and-build

In design-and-build contracts, the client or project promoter is able to set out specific requirements for environmental protection, but this seldom happens, because the responsibility lies wholly with the contractor in this type of contract. By default, any consideration of environmental matters falls to the contractor. When briefing the designer, the contractor may make specific reference to environmental protection measures and means of protecting the aquatic environment. However, in general there is little incentive to do so unless specific difficulties are anticipated.

4.1.2 Partnering

Partnering contracts seem to provide the best opportunity to ensure that environmental protection is an integral part of both the design and construction phases of a project. The philosophy of preventing pollution coincides with that of collaboratively applied foresight. All parties can be made aware of the issues at the outset if it is stated that environmental protection – and preferably environmental improvement – is one of the objectives defined within the partnering agreement.

4.1.3   Special requirements

Some contract forms allow for the insertion of "special requirements" or "special conditions". These documents, often provided by statutory undertakers and utility companies, relate to the protection of their plant and equipment. However, it is feasible to prepare a set of documents in this style that state the environmental regulator's basic requirements for the protection of the aquatic environment during construction. Each document might address a specific activity such as demolition, earthworks, drainage works, working on contaminated sites or routine maintenance. The document would be bound into the contract in the same way as existing "special requirements", thereby giving it some force. In addition, it would be necessary to provide an item in the bill of quantities to allow the contractor to price the cost of complying with these requirements.

The most effective means of ensuring that these matters are addressed may be to prepare a series of "special requirements for the protection of the aquatic environment". These would be provided to developers, contractors, architects, engineers, planning consultants and others at the earliest possible stage of the project, when consultation with the environmental regulator begins.

It has to be recognised that this approach will not have any immediate significant effect on the multitude of small construction sites, building maintenance works, drain installation and repair operations, cable and utilities works, and many other small, daily activities. This will only be achieved over a longer period by a general increase in environmental awareness within the construction industry and further training.

4.1.4   Improving control

Contract forms could play a greater role in protecting the environment. The simplest improvement would be the addition of a clause or special requirement reminding the contractor of their statutory duty to protect the environment and to prevent pollution.

A more positive approach would be to require the contractor to prepare a detailed method statement setting out how they propose to prevent aquatic pollution. This would be provided with the tender and evaluated as part of the contractor selection process.

A further step would be to list specific requirements or matters for consideration, eg:

- watercourses to be protected
- aquifer status at the site
- location of nearby water abstractions
- points where crossings of watercourses are to be permitted
- specific requirements of the environment regulator
- fuel storage
- water quality monitoring requirements
- flora and fauna to be protected
- staff training.

In some cases these requirements should be highlighted in the "instructions to tenderers", particularly if the response is to be used as part of the tender evaluation process.

In the same vein, clients could also require tenderers to provide evidence of good environmental performance in the past, either as part of the tender process or at the pre-qualification stage when tenderers are invited to bid.

A set of environmental performance criteria might include:

- past prosecutions and fines
- accredited environmental management systems, such as ISO 14001
- client references
- regulator references
- awards and commendations
- staff training policy and manuals
- environmental policy statements
- available specialist support
- emergency plans
- ability to provide appropriately trained and experienced staff
- past project experience.

4.2 ICE CONTRACTS

4.2.1 ICE 5th and 6th editions

The Institution of Civil Engineers (ICE) *Conditions of contract* 5th edition has been in use since the early 1970s. In 1988, the conditions were comprehensively revised, but the ICE 6th edition does not introduce significant changes in the balance of responsibilities between the parties. A substantial proportion of the document was rewritten to remove anomalies and improve clarity.

The ICE *Conditions of contract* forms an agreement between the employer and the contractor. The employer's role is limited to matters such as nominating the engineer, consenting to assignments, making payment upon certificates and giving notice to determine the contractor's employment.

The *Conditions of contract* can be, and frequently is, supplemented with special conditions. This is where those drafting the contract may well choose to include environmental requirements such as the control of water pollution from the site. Equal weight is given to all terms of the contract and, hence, an identical effect would be produced by including any additional terms in any other document.

Under the ICE *Conditions of contract*, the contractor is generally responsible for all aspects of the requirements to complete the works. This usually includes the design of temporary works and the adequacy, stability and safety of all site operations and methods of construction. The contractor is not responsible for the design or specification of the permanent works except as expressly provided in the contract. With more contracts being let on a design-and-build basis, it has become far more common for the contractor to be responsible for the design of the permanent works as well.

The contract is administered by the engineer, who is not a direct party to the contract although the contract describes the duties and authority of the engineer and his/her representative (the resident engineer). The engineer has no authority to alter the terms of the contract unless a clause to this effect is specifically included in it.

A problem associated with this type of contract may arise when the terms effectively leave the engineer, as the agent, with very little or no actual authority. This allows the contractor to pick and choose, on a commercial basis, which parts of the contract they wish to comply with. The commercial pressure is to comply only with the requirements in relation to the completed works that will be valued by the engineer for payment. Consequently, temporary works that are not measured in the contract for specific payment, such as environmental mitigation measures during construction, may be carried out in a half-hearted way or completely ignored.

There is a difference in this regard between the ICE 5th and 6th editions. The ICE 5th edition makes no specific reference to pollution and states in Clause 29 (2):

> *All work shall be carried out without unreasonable noise and disturbance. The Contractor shall indemnify the Employer from and against any liability for damages on account of noise or other disturbance created while or in carrying out the work and from and against all claims demands proceedings damages costs charges and expenses whatever in regard or in relation to such liability.*

This clearly states where responsibility lies within the contract – with the contractor.

The 6th edition introduces a specific reference to "pollution" (in Clause 29(4)). However, the responsibility for pollution that "is not the unavoidable consequence of constructing and completing the Works" is placed on the contractor. The clause states:

> *The Employer shall indemnify the Contractor from and against any liability for damages on account of noise disturbance or other pollution which is the unavoidable consequence of carrying out the Works and against all claims demands proceedings damages costs charges and expenses whatsoever in regard or in relation to such liability.*

In theory, the employer is shouldering some responsibility for the pollution that might be caused by the works. However, if the engineer has consulted and included appropriate measures within the contract there should be no "unavoidable consequences" and the responsibility will revert back to the contractor.

As the contract places the responsibility on the contractor, both the employer and the engineer may well consider themselves to be protected from any serious repercussions from inaction. Responsibility for pollution incidents from construction sites thus remains with the contractor when this type of contract is used, despite the detailed pre-planning and requirements of the conditions of contract.

4.2.2   ICE *Minor works* 2nd edition

ICE's *Conditions of contract for minor works* is essentially a concise version of the 6th edition. As the title suggests, it is intended for minor works of more modest value where:

- the potential risks involved in the works for both the employer and the contractor are adjudged to be small

- the works are of a simple and straightforward nature

- the design of the works, save for any design work for which the contractor is made responsible, is complete in all essentials before tenders are invited

- the contractor has no responsibility for the design of the permanent works other than possibly design of a specialist nature

- nominated subcontractors are not employed

- the contract value does not exceed £250 000 and the period for completion of the contract does not exceed six months, except where the method of payment is on either a day-work or a cost plus fee basis.

Although based on the ICE 6th edition there are significant differences in the *Conditions of contract for minor works*. In particular, the balance of risk is to a great extent shared. This is presumably on the basis that risks are small and that on a small project of short duration a contractor cannot be expected to cover the cost of checking all possible risks.

The contract is an agreement between the employer and the contractor and is administered by the engineer, who has to be a named individual notified by the employer to the contractor in writing.

The employer's role is limited to that of nominating the engineer, consenting to assignments, making payment upon certificates and giving notice to determine the contractor's employment. It should be noted that there is no mention of a contractor's agent. The notes for guidance issued with the ICE *Conditions of contract for minor works* make it clear that a contractor may not have an agent permanently on site. Instructions may need to be issued to the contractor's head office or, in an urgent situation, given directly to the contractor's operatives.

Included with the *Conditions of contract for minor works* are an agreement, contract schedule and appendix. The contract schedule lists the documents forming the contract:

- the agreement (if any)
- the contractor's tender
- the conditions of contract
- the appendix to the conditions of contract
- the drawings
- the specification
- a bill of quantities or some form of schedule of rates or dayworks.

There is no provision for amendments or additions of the conditions of contract, and the guidance notes specifically recommend that this should be avoided.

As in the 6th edition, the contract is administered by the engineer, who is not a direct party to the contract and has no authority to alter the terms of the contract. However, the engineer has the power to give instructions affecting the works, and these are clearly set out. As there is no provision for amendments or additions to the conditions of contract, this power is unlikely to be reduced by an employer.

Problems of the engineer lacking authority are unlikely to arise with the *Conditions of contract for minor works*. Responsibility for statutory obligations are shared between the employer and the contractor. Under Section 9, "Statutory obligations" in Clause 9.1 makes the contractor responsible for all notices and costs thereof. However, in Clause 9.2 it is stated that the employer is responsible for obtaining, in due time, all consents etc. In Clause 9.3 the contractor is not liable for any failure to comply where that failure results from carrying out the works in accordance with the contract. Also, in Clause 10.4, the contractor is not liable to indemnify the employer for "damage which is the unavoidable result of the construction of the Works in accordance with the Contract".

To protect the employer from responsibility in the event of a pollution problem, the designer should have ensured that suitable precautions were included in the works. However, as the ICE *Conditions of contract for minor works* are specifically designed for small-scale works with little risk and of a straightforward nature, it may well be that the designer has not identified any perceived problem of this nature. The pressures of time and cost may have resulted in the designer not consulting with the environment regulator on the mitigation measures required. When appropriate mitigation works are not included in the original contract, it falls to the engineer to give timely instructions for such works as may be necessary. As it is likely that neither the engineer, engineer's representative or the agent are on site full-time, however, it appears that responsibility falls to the contractor's operatives to be vigilant. The contractor's operatives may well consider that such matters are not their responsibility.

It appears that this form of contract is not suitable for use where pollution may be a significant issue.

4.3   *THE ENGINEERING AND CONSTRUCTION CONTRACT (ECC),* SECOND EDITION, NOVEMBER 1995

The *Engineering and Construction Contract (ECC)*, 2nd edition, November 1995, was drafted for the ICE to reflect the many changes in contract strategies that have been taking effect in the construction industry in the past 10–15 years. Commissioned in 1986, it has gone through an extended development and consultation period and includes the recommendations of the Latham (1994) Report, *Constructing the team*. Although the second edition was published in November 1995, it is still neither universally used nor accepted. However, it is the intention of the ICE that the *ECC* should be widely adopted in engineering and construction generally. The intention is that the *ECC* should be flexible, clear and simple, and a stimulus to good management.

The *ECC* is a family of documents that are designed to be put together in a variety of ways depending on the requirements of the contract and the proposed method of procurement. The contract is between the employer and the contractor but is administered by a "project manager". Unlike many other forms of contract, the roles of designer, manager, supervisor and adjudicator are separate. The roles of designer, manager and supervisor may be combined, but the role of adjudicator may not.

The opening paragraph of all versions of the contract reads:

> *10.1 The Employer, the Contractor, the Project Manager and the Supervisor shall act as stated in the Contract and in a spirit of mutual trust and co-operation. The Adjudicator shall act as stated in this Contract and in a spirit of independence.*

These expressions of co-operation and trust are radical departures from traditional adversarial contracts. The use of plain English rather than legal jargon is unusual, too.

The *ECC* is intended to:

- be used for engineering and construction work containing any or all of the traditional disciplines such as civil, building, electrical and mechanical work
- be used whether the contractor has some design responsibility, full design responsibility or no design responsibility
- provide all the normal current options for types of contract, such as competitive tender (where the contractor is committed to his/her offered prices), target contracts, cost reimbursable contracts and management contracts
- be used in the UK and in other countries.

The *ECC* has been designed on the assumption that work may be subcontracted. A standard form of subcontract called the *NEC Engineering and construction subcontract (ECS)* (1995) has been published. This is very similar to the *ECC* but uses appropriate names for the parties and has a few additional provisions appropriate to a subcontract.

Two specific changes from conventional construction practice deserve mention. First, although subcontractors are permitted, they cannot be nominated. This change is made to simplify contract arrangements and to eliminate the clouding of responsibilities that nomination causes. This should not only reduce disputes but also strengthen the motivation of the parties to manage their activities. An employer who has reasons for using a particular contractor for part of the works can use the *ECC* for a direct contract alongside other contractors.

Second, the financial control document in the *ECC* can be either a traditional bill of quantities or an activity schedule. The activity schedule is a list of items with lump sum prices. The total price for the work to be done is divided between each of the items. This is a simpler document to prepare and use than the traditional bill. Neither document is used in the *ECC* for any purpose other than assessing payments due to the contractor.

The *ECC* sets out the responsibilities and roles of the following parties:

- the employer
- the project manager
- the supervisor
- the contractor
- the subcontractor
- the adjudicator.

Separate functions of the employer's and contractor's designers are assumed but not mentioned in the contract. The role played by the engineer, architect or supervising officer in other standard forms is divided between the project manager, the supervisor, the employer's designer and the adjudicator.

The project manager is appointed by the employer, either from their own staff or from outside. His/her role within the *ECC* is to manage the contract for the employer with the intention of achieving the employer's objectives for the completed project.

The *ECC* places considerable authority in the hands of the project manager. It assumes that they have the employer's authority to carry out actions and make decisions as necessary. If the contract with the employer constrains the project manager in any way, as for example in the case of a limit on the amount of payment that they may authorise as a compensation event assessment, the project manager is responsible for ensuring that all the approvals are given in time to comply with the time periods set out in the *ECC*. If such approvals by the employer are not given, the contractor has the right to raise the matter with the adjudicator.

The contractual role of the project manager is defined in terms of the actions and decisions they can take. They are constrained from acting unreasonably in this role by statements on the type of decision they can make. If the contractor believes that any of the project manager's actions or decisions is not in accordance with the contract, they may refer it to the adjudicator (Clause 90.1).

Perhaps the strongest feature of the *ECC*, and one that stimulates co-operation rather than adversarial activity, is the fact that the contractor has little concern with the way the project manager decides to deal with problems that are the employer's responsibility. If the contractor's eventual payment is largely secure, they are not encouraged to make the worst of any problems that arise, as regards their effect either upon cost or upon the timing of the work. This feature is strengthened by the flexibility available to the employer and the project manager in their pre-contract choice of main option for a particular contract, ranging from price commitment to cost-reimbursable. The *ECC* permits this choice of contract strategy without the need to resort to different standard forms.

Although the employer appoints the designers, the contract between the employer and the contractor does not refer to the employer's designer.

The employer and the contractor jointly appoint the adjudicator, who becomes involved only when a dispute is referred to them. Being independent of both employer and contractor, they are required to give a decision on the dispute, within stated time limits.

The contractor provides the works in accordance with the works information contained in the contract. The contractor may or may not be responsible for some or all of the design.

The *ECC* permits subcontractors, but not nominated subcontractors. They have to be approved by the project manager, but, if the contractor subcontracts work, the contractor is responsible under the contract for that work (Clause 26.1).

There is no specific reference to pollution or consultation with outside bodies within the contract. However, there are relatively clear definitions of general responsibilities. Obtaining outside approval is the employer's responsibility, and would be expected to be a duty of the project manager. The contractor would only be responsible for outside approval where the contractor is also responsible for the design.

It is assumed that the employer would be responsible for all mitigation measures to ensure non-pollution, except for the case where the contractor is also the designer. In this case, the contractor would be responsible for all mitigation measures.

In this form of contract, with responsibility clearly identified, it is unlikely that mitigation measures could be ignored once they were included in the contract. The authority of the project manager is clear. It would be their responsibility to give timely instructions to the contractor to ensure compliance with any mitigation measures required. Failure to do so would leave the employer liable. There is no financial reward in the case of a contractor ignoring mitigation measures or carrying them out in a half-hearted way that did not meet the requirements of the mitigation. There are mechanisms within the contract whereby the cost of these works, as adjudicated independently, could be reimbursed from the payments they might otherwise have received. Deliberate non-action relating to mitigation measures is therefore much less likely from the *ECC* contract than would be the case in more traditional types of contract.

4.4 GENERAL CONDITIONS OF CONTRACT FOR WATER INDUSTRY PLANT CONTRACTS, FORM G/90

The G/90 *General conditions* are recommended by the Water Services Association of England and Wales (1990) for water industry lump sum plant contracts. A form of this contract has been in use since 1976. The most recent version of the *General conditions* was issued in October 1990. It contains amendments that were recommended by the Institution of Mechanical Engineers, the Institution of Electrical Engineers, the Association of Consulting Engineers, the National Water Council, the British Electrical and Allied Manufacturers' Association, the British Pump Manufacturers' Association and the British Water and Effluent Treatment Plant Association, and further amendments by the Additional and Substitute Clauses recommended by the Water Services Association in 1989.

The *General conditions* are intended to be used in a contract between the employer, referred to as the purchaser, and the contractor.

The engineer is given very clear and specific authority to manage and direct the works under the individual clauses of the *General conditions*. The purchaser is required to notify the contractor in writing of the identity of the engineer. The engineer is to supervise the works and, once the purchaser has accepted the tender, the engineers gives all the necessary instructions and orders to the contractor. The engineer is permitted to delegate to an engineer's representative or clerk of works. The contractor is required to have a representative on site during working hours.

There are no specific references to mitigation works and the person responsible for obtaining permission from third parties is not identified. Under Clauses 23(i) "Insurance of Works" and 23(vi) "Damage to Persons and Property", the contractor is required to insure the purchasers against all claims. Clause 21(i) "Liability for Accidents and Damages" makes the contractor responsible for the care of the works. Clause 21(iv) and (v) "Indemnification" states:

> *"21(iv) Subject to Clause 22, the Contractor shall be liable for and shall indemnify and keep the Purchaser indemnified from and against all loss, damage or injury to any person or to any property whatsoever (including property forming part of the Works for which the Contractor is responsible under Sub-Clause (i) of this Clause except during the period of such responsibility) and against all actions, suits, claims, damages, demands, costs, charges and expenses arising in connection therewith which shall:*
>
> > *(a) occur at any time before all the Works have been taken over under Clause 28 (Taking Over) and be occasioned by or arise out of or in consequence of the carrying out of the Works or fault, defect, error or omission in any design (other than a design made or furnished by the Purchaser and for which the Contractor has disclaimed responsibility in writing within a reasonable time after the receipt of the Purchaser's instructions), materials or workmanship. Provided that the Contractor's liability to indemnify the Purchaser as aforesaid shall be reduced proportionately to the extent that any act or neglect of the Purchaser, his/her servants or agents has contributed to the said loss, damage or injury or that such loss, damage or injury has been the inevitable result of the carrying out of the Works in accordance with the Contract; or*
> >
> > *(b) occur within three years of all the Works having been taken over and be occasioned by or arise out of any act or default or breach of statutory duty of the Contractor, his/her servants or subcontractors or fault, defect, error or omission in any design (other than a design made, furnished or specified by the Purchaser and for which the Contractor has disclaimed responsibility in writing within a reasonable time after the receipt of the Purchaser's instructions), materials or workmanship.*
> >
> > *Provided that the liability of the Contractor to indemnify the Purchaser under this Sub-Clause in respect of damage to the Purchaser's property shall be limited to direct physical damage to such property.*
> >
> > *There shall be no limit on the liability of the Contractor to indemnify the Purchaser under this Clause 21(v) save where the Purchaser and the Contractor have agreed an upper limit to such liability and such upper limit is entered in the Appendix.*
>
> *21(v) In the event of any claim being made against the Purchaser arising out of the matters referred to and in respect of which the Contractor may be liable under this Clause, the Contractor shall be promptly notified thereof, and may*

at his/her own expense conduct all negotiations for the settlement of the same and any litigation that may arise therefrom. The Purchaser shall not, unless and until the Contractor shall have failed to take over the conduct of the negotiations or litigation make any admissions which might be prejudicial thereto. The conduct by the Contractor of such negotiations or litigation shall be conditional upon the Contractor having first given to the Purchaser such reasonable security as shall from time to time be required by the Purchaser to cover the amount ascertained or agreed or estimated, as the case may be, of any compensation, damages, expenses and costs of which the Purchaser may become liable. The Purchaser shall, at the request of the Contractor, afford all available assistance for any such purpose, and shall be repaid all reasonable expenses incurred in so doing."

This makes the contractor responsible except in the specific case where the contractor has disclaimed responsibility beforehand in writing for design supplied by the purchasers and to the extent that the purchaser contributed to the damage.

The engineer would be responsible for ensuring that the purchaser was not liable for any portion of damages by liaising with the environment regulator and others on the mitigation measures required. The engineer should ensure that these measures are included in the contract or timely instructions are given.

There might be commercial benefit in the contractor ignoring such mitigation measures or in performing them in a half-hearted way. However, with the engineer's authority and powers so clearly stated, it is unlikely that the engineer would not give instructions for mitigation works to be expedited. The contractor would have to specifically disregard the instructions of an empowered engineer in order to avoid carrying out such mitigation measures. Deliberate refusal to effect mitigation measures is thus less likely under the G/90 *General conditions* than, say, within the ICE 5th and 6th editions.

4.5 INSTITUTION OF CHEMICAL ENGINEERS (IChemE)

***Model form of conditions of contract for process plants suitable for lump sum contracts* (known as the "Red Book")**

***Model form of conditions of contract for process plant suitable for reimbursible contracts* (known as the "Green Book")**

The Institution of Chemical Engineers (IChemE) produced its original *Model form of conditions of contract for process plants suitable for lump sum contracts in the UK* in 1968. Subsequently known as the "Red Book", it was reissued in 1981 and 1995. Its success prompted publication in 1976 of the *Model form* suitable for reimbursable contracts, which became known as the "Green Book" and was reissued in 1992. These model forms broke new ground by attempting to deal with the complex way in which the "employer" – referred to as the purchaser – and the "contractor" divided responsibility.

The IChemE *Model forms* are an agreement between the purchaser and the contractor. Other persons described in the contract include:

- project manager
- project manager's representative
- contractor's contract manager
- contractor's site manager.

Although the project manager may be a consultant outside the direct employment of the purchaser, it is normal for them to be an employee of the purchaser. The *Model form* states that:

> *any obligation stated under the Contract to be an obligation of the Project Manager shall be deemed to be an obligation of the Purchaser. The Purchaser shall be responsible for any act, neglect or omission of the Project Manager as if it were an act, neglect or omission of the Purchaser. In all matters where the Project Manager is required or authorised under the Contract to exercise his/her discretion or make a judgement or form an opinion he shall do so to the best of his/her skill and judgement as a professional engineer and shall be impartial as between the Purchaser and Contractor.*

The purchaser and the project manager may be construed to be one and the same. If the project manager is not an employee of the purchaser, the purchaser cannot subsequently change the project manager to an employee without the contractor's consent. This is presumably a safeguard for the contractor in the case of a purchaser changing the balance of an agreement.

The project manager may, by notice to the contractor, authorise the project manager's representative to exercise any of the powers and functions of the project manager under the contract.

The project manager's authority is clearly stated:

> *Subject to the provisions of the Contractor, the Project Manager may at any time instruct the Contractor to execute the Works or any part thereof as the Project Manager may decide and the Contractor shall comply with such instruction within a reasonable period to be agreed between the Project Manager and the Contractor.*

The limitations on their authority are few.

The contractor's contract manager is required to have full authority to act on the contractor's behalf and their appointment cannot be terminated without the consent of the project manager. It is also a contractual requirement that a suitable person is employed at the site as site manager for the whole period of the contract. The site manager must supervise the contractor's work and receive instructions from the project manager or the project manager's representative. The site manager may not be changed without the previous consent or requirement of the project manager.

Where specialist experience is required to carry out a project, the model forms allow the purchaser to nominate not only the contracts manager but also key engineering and/or construction supervisory staff. Once nominated, such staff cannot be substituted without the prior consent of the project manager.

The contract comprises:

- form of agreement (if completed)
- general conditions of contract
- special conditions (if any)
- specification and documentation (if any)
- schedules (including cost elements and rates and charges if a reimbursable contract).

The details of the contracts differ according to whether it is a lump sum or a reimbursable contract, but the responsibilities are similar. Assignment and subcontracting, including nominated subcontractors, are a permitted aspect of the contract, although initial consent is generally required. However, it is clear that the contractor carries the responsibility of fulfilling the terms of the contract irrespective of the performance of any subcontractor.

The responsibility for complying with relevant laws and other controls is shared. The contract requires that purchaser and contractor comply with all relevant laws, statutes, bylaws, regulations and other measures having the force of law and to ensure that on completion the plant also complies. The purchaser is responsible for obtaining all permissions required from local owners of real property and any government or local authority for the use of the site for construction, operation and maintenance.

Although responsibility is shared, the purchaser is required to liaise with the environment regulator and others on any mitigation measures and to include these in the contract. Should such mitigation be overlooked, it is the project manager's responsibility to give timely instructions for the measures to be included during the contract.

With responsibility clearly identified, it is unlikely that mitigation measures would be ignored once they are included in the contract. The authority of the project manager is clear. However, there could be a substantially different reaction from the contractor depending on whether it is a lump sum or reimbursable contract. In a lump sum contract, where the mitigation measures were of a temporary nature, the contractor might have a financial incentive for trying to get away with as little as possible. The converse might be true for a reimbursable contract, where the financial incentive might be to do as much as possible, in order to claim back from the purchaser.

4.6   *STANDARD FORM OF BUILDING CONTRACT* (JCT 80)

The Joint Contracts Tribunal (JCT) is a body formed from representatives of the following organisations:

- Association of Consulting Engineers
- British Property Federation
- Construction Confederation
- Local Government Association
- National Specialist Contractors Council
- Royal Institute of British Architects
- Royal Institution of Chartered Surveyors
- Scottish Building Contract Committee.

The JCT produces a range of contracts for the building industry. They include contracts for small, medium and large schemes, contracts for traditional procurement methods, as well as those for design-and-build

The JCT publishes the *Standard form of building contract* (1980 edition) for major building work, which follows the traditional method of procurement. The contractor is responsible for carrying out the work, and design is substantially in the hands of the architect. The employer can require the contractor to tender a lump sum price, or give an indication only of price at tender stage with the work re-measured as executed and priced on the basis of rates set out in bills of approximate quantities.

The form is published in several versions for use by the private sector or by local authorities, and with quantities, with approximate quantities, or without quantities.

The contract makes provision for the nomination of both subcontractors and suppliers. Where a project involves work that may demand a subcontractor with special design experience and technical expertise, this facility for the employer to choose who is to do the work might be very useful. However, because of the intricacies of tendering, the programme, design responsibility and subcontract provisions, the procedures set out in the main contract need to be followed carefully. The various subcontract documents published by the JCT are intended for use with subcontractors.

The form can be adapted by the incorporation of separately published supplements, but care is needed as they are not necessarily mutually compatible. The administrative procedures under JCT80 are quite complicated and should be followed carefully. JCT does issue practice notices and administration forms to assist those using JCT80 contracts.

The JCT80 contract is one between the employer and contractor. Other persons described in the contract include:

- architect
- contract administrator
- quantity surveyor
- person-in-charge
- clerk of works
- planning supervisor
- principal contractor.

If an architect is used, then the contract administrator is deleted from the contract and vice versa. There is no particular requirement that any of the above be an individual, although in the case of a local authority employer this might be more appropriate where personnel come from the same department.

The contract is administered by the architect or contract administrator. The employer's role is generally limited to matters such as nominating the architect or contract administrator, making payments upon certificates and giving notice to determine the contractor's employment.

Under the JCT80, the contractor is generally responsible for all aspects of the requirements of the building work, normally including the design of all temporary works and the adequacy, stability and safety of all building works. The contractor is not responsible for the design or specification of the building, except as expressly provided in the contract.

The contract is administered by the architect or the contracts administrator, who is not a direct party to the contract, although their duties are clearly set out in it. The quantity surveyor is required to measure and value the works, but has no relevant administrative authority within the contract. It is a requirement that the contractor always has a person-in-charge on site, who is responsible for taking instructions from the architect/contracts administrator or clerk of works. The clerk of works can give instructions and have some authority delegated from the architect, but any instruction must be confirmed in writing by the architect within two days in writing.

Under Clause 6, "Statutory obligations, notices fees and charges", the contractor is:

Subject to Clause 6.1.5, the Contractor shall comply with and give all notices required by, any Act of Parliament, any instrument, rule or order made under any Act of Parliament, or any regulation or by-law of any local authority or of any statutory undertaker which has any jurisdiction with regard to the Works or with whose systems the same are or will be connected (all requirements to be so complied with being referred to in the Conditions as 'the Statutory Requirements').

JCT80 makes no specific reference to pollution and states in Clause 20.2, "Injury to persons and property and indemnity to employer":

20.2 The Contractor shall, subject to Clause 20.3 and, where applicable, Clause 22C.1, be liable for, and shall indemnify the Employer against, any expense, liability, loss, claim or proceedings in respect of any injury or damage whatsoever to any property real or personal insofar as such injury or damage arises out of or in the course of or by reason of the carrying out of the Works, and to the extent that the same is due to any negligence, breach of statutory duty, omission or default of the Contractor, his/her servants or agents or of any person employed or engaged upon or in connection with the Works or any part thereof, his/her servants or agents or of any other person who may properly be on the site upon or in connection with the Works or any part thereof, his/her servants or agents, other than the Employer or any person employed, engaged or authorised by him or by any local authority or statutory undertaker executing work solely in pursuance of its statutory rights or obligations.

The contract puts considerable emphasis on insurance, and Sections 21 and 22 provide clauses for a full range of options, in an effort to cover all eventualities. Clauses for the following insurance are included:

- insurance of the works, including cases for:
    - nominated subcontractors
    - domestic subcontractors
    - joint name policies
    - specified perils

- erection of new buildings; all-risk insurance of the works by the contractor, including cases for:
    - joint names
    - single policy
    - annual policy
    - use of insurance monies

- erection of new buildings; all-risk insurance of the works by the employer, including cases for:
    - joint names
    - rights of the contractor
    - payment by the employer

- insurance of existing structures; insurance of works in or extensions to existing structures, including cases for the employer to insure for:
    - joint names for existing structures
    - joint names for extensions
    - rights of contractor
    - payment by employer

- insurance of the employer's loss of liquidated damages.

This emphasis on trying to cover all eventualities by insurance perhaps reflects the make-up of the JCT constituent bodies. It presupposes that there will be problems and accidents but ensures that insurance cover will be available to pay for the necessary remedial work or compensation. There is little consideration within the JCT contract for taking action to avoid the problem or accident in the first place.

Although pollution is not mentioned, any incident would clearly be the responsibility of the contractor. However, a well-insured contractor may not consider avoiding pollution a high priority. Presumably, responsible parties entering into a JCT80 contract would try to avoid causing pollution. The architect or consultant contributing to the building work would consult with the various authorities concerned with environmental matters and they would be included in the contract. If the work is remeasured, there are clear financial advantages in the contractor ensuring temporary environmental protection works are carried out properly. If the work is not remeasured, there may not be any financial incentive to carry out the work properly or at all.

In terms of protecting the environment from pollution incidents, the JCT80 contracts leave a lot to be desired. Other than the financial pressure from large fines or the cost of insurance, there is little incentive to take proper care. Both financial pressure and education of all parties using the *Standard form of building contract* (JCT80) is probably needed if fewer pollution events are to be expected from the building industry.

4.7   PARTNERING

In recent years, the idea of partnering has grown in popularity and has been successfully used to gain significant benefits for those involved in construction projects. The general idea is that the main parties involved in a construction contract agree to use their best endeavours to carry out the project in the most cost-effective, beneficial manner. Those involved are encouraged to share information, trust each other and always act in the best interest of the project, rather than their separate interests.

By sharing environmental responsibilities, cost savings can be made. A positive relationship between employer, designer and contractor can help to resolve environmental problems more easily and cost-effectively.

The partnering agreement is separate from whatever construction contract is used between employer and contractor. However, it is difficult to envisage partnering being particularly successful with traditional adversarial contracts, such as the ICE 5th and 6th editions, or the JCT80. Partnering has been reported as operating very successfully using the *ECC*. This is understandable, as this form of contract has been drafted specifically to encourage good management and co-operation between the partners to obtain the objectives of the employer. The two principles on which the *ECC* is based and which impact upon the objective of stimulating good management are:

- foresight applied collaboratively mitigates problems and shrinks risk

- clear division of function and responsibility helps accountability and motivates people to play their part.

These are of course exactly the sort of objectives that would give true meaning to the idea of partnering.

The employer would have an *ECC* contract with the contractor; a "target contract with activity schedule" would be appropriate. The employer would also have a professional service contract with the project manager and designer. Separate to these contracts would be a partnering agreement, typically between the employer, contractor and designer. This agreement would in simple terms state the objectives of the project and state that the parties would work in a spirit of trust and co-operation to achieve that goal. Based on the target cost of the project, there would be an agreement to share cost savings or overruns on the basis of their respective share of the cost of the scheme. At the completion of the contract, the target cost, plus the compensation costs, would be added together to give the out-turn value. The out-turn value would be compared to the actual cost of the project. If there was a saving or an overrun, the parties would benefit or contribute in accordance with their agreement.

The fact that a partnering agreement has been entered into would make it less likely for one party to ignore an environmental problem once it was identified by one of the partners. In addition, it is more likely that discussions between the designers and those concerned with environmental matters will be passed on to the contractor at some stage. This helps avoid a common complaint from environmental agencies that, although they discuss, advise and agree courses of action with designers, that information has difficulty in reaching the person actually performing the work.

5 Managing water pollution from construction

5.1 INTRODUCTION

Pollution incidents originating from construction sites are avoidable. Clean-up and remediation following a pollution event on a construction site can carry an extremely high cost. In contrast, early evaluation of the site and the operations that are to be carried out there and the development of a comprehensive site operating plan covering the pollution risks and prevention measures, is usually relatively inexpensive. Ideally, this is carried out at the planning stage.

To manage water pollution from construction sites, the whole life of the project should be considered, from conception through to completion.

5.2 THE CONSTRUCTION CYCLE

The construction cycle can be defined as the sequence of events or activities carried out in the development and implementation of a construction project (see Figure 5.1).

The construction cycle presented in this book is based on a project procured under a typical traditional contract. It comprises two key stages: pre-construction and construction. In very general terms, a consultant is responsible for designing and planning the works in the pre-construction stage and a contractor for implementing the designs and plans in the construction stage.

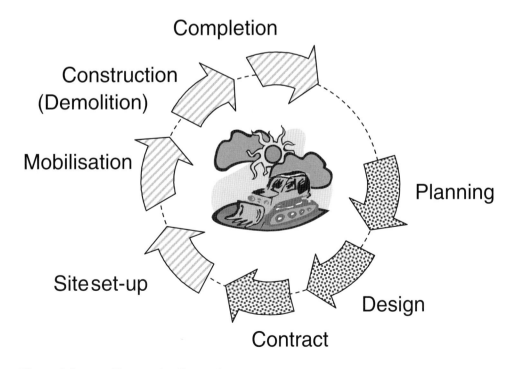

Figure 5.1   *The construction cycle*

The cycle begins with the appointment of a consultant and finishes with the completion of works on site by the contractor and handover to client. It is described under the following headings: planning, design, contract, site set-up, mobilisation, construction, completion and demobilisation. This construction cycle assumes that appropriate development consents have not been obtained. It does not include project feasibility, site selection and site purchase; nor does it consider issues such as the source and availability of construction materials and their transport to site.

The examination of the potential pollution risks throughout the life of the construction project should follow several logical steps. These steps are introduced below. The importance of each element varies between individual construction sites and depends upon geographical location, sensitivity of the surrounding aquatic environment and the size and scale of the project. It is important to know at what point in the construction cycle water pollution issues must be tackled (Figure 6.15). Some elements of pollution prevention may fall to both the designer/consultant and to the contractor.

At the end of each of the following sections, a box provides examples of the best management practices that apply.

5.2.1   Planning

At the conceptual and planning stages it is essential to examine the proximity of the site to controlled waters, such as streams, aquifers and water abstractions. The historical use of the site and the likelihood of contaminating materials being present should highlight the issues that ought to be considered in the detailed design stage. Note that dewatering activities and site runoff may draw contamination into the site from adjacent locations (see Sections 2.5.1 and 2.5.2).

The early examination of the potential for water pollution will facilitate the design of site layout and expected operations. Thus the planning stages will identify areas that may be particularly sensitive to aquatic pollution during construction. This is also an ideal time to discuss the identified potential water pollution issues directly with the relevant regulatory authorities. A major development may require an environmental impact assessment (EIA) and the preparation of an environmental statement (ES) for submission to the planning authority. Where this is not required, the preparation of an environmental management plan is beneficial and may even be required by the client. The environment regulator may require the contractor to monitor discharge volumes and quality (see Section 5.4.1).

The scheme promoters should be encouraged to undertake studies to identify possible historic pollution as early as possible in the consideration of each project. Where potential contaminated land issues are identified, they should be examined in greater detail by means of a qualitative risk assessment that identifies the source, pathway and target. Typical mitigation measures are illustrated in Figure 6.16.

Best management practice

- Identify the location of all controlled waters, such as streams, aquifers and abstractions close to the works

- Identify the location and type/grade of surface water features present now and in the past at the site and its environs

- Consider the sources, pathways and impacts or targets of potential pollution

- Investigate historical uses of the site and nearby areas to identify contaminated land

- Include the whole life-cycle of construction projects from planning to completion (including demolition and site clearance)

- As early as possible in the project, discuss with the relevant environment regulator the potential pollution sources and mitigation measures required

- Prepare an environmental management plan or an environmental statement if required by the planning process

- Plan ahead, determine what consents and licences are needed, and obtain them.

5.2.2   Design

By including the elements identified in the planning stage, the design stage addresses the issues pertinent to potential water pollution. Among the elements that can be included are the ground conditions, the design of phased construction to minimise earthmoving, the season during which work will take place, the protection of controlled waters and the design of proposed water control measures. The design should take into account the way in which the construction will be executed, and be sympathetic to the construction techniques and space available on site. Wherever possible, environmental considerations should be balanced with other constraints. Although the contractor is responsible for decisions about the construction techniques to be used, the scheme should be designed with water pollution issues in mind.

The project design should provide solutions that minimise the risk of pollutants entering the aquatic environment from the construction site. The construction works can proceed more smoothly if assessments are made of the proximity of the site to controlled waters and vulnerable sewerage systems discharging to controlled waters, the site topography and the careful design of the works. Sympathetic construction techniques and phased working to minimise the sources of potential pollution from the site can play both an active and a passive role in the operation of the construction site (see Case study 19).

Case study 19 ☺   *Change of design to accommodate environmental constraints*

A major road scheme that crossed numerous rivers and watercourses designated as SSSIs and with very high water quality raised several construction issues. The permanent works were to a standard design that did not consider detailed buildability, not knowing the contractors' preferred method of working. Some of the environmental constraints were unknown at the time of design. The early involvement of the contractor, consultant and environmental specialists enabled the permanent works to be modified to ensure easier, more environment-sensitive construction, for example:

- large-diameter augered piles were considered inappropriate in a low-lying flood plane with 4 m of peat and alluvium overlying gravel and chalk. Concerns related to cement or bentonite stabilisation leaching into the gravel aquifer and chalk slurry being created by the piling process. A driven pile alternative was developed.

- permanent sheet piling was enhanced to allow it to be used as a temporary cutoff wall for permanent foundations adjacent to a river.

Included in the passive design criteria is designing the construction project to cause as little disturbance as possible. This may take the form selection of foundations that are sympathetic to the local aquatic environment and split-level construction to reduce potential mass earthmoving operations. The latter is as applicable to small projects such as house construction as to large-scale industrial sites and highways.

Active design elements may include the design of earthworks to be a "strip and place" operation where possible. In this process, to prevent the reworking of material, stripped topsoil and subsoil are placed and formed directly in a "final location", which also allows immediate reseeding and planting.

Stripped material may be suitable for use as site bunds to collect and attenuate the impact of water entering and leaving the site.

Discussions with the relevant environment regulator at this stage can provide a series of guidelines for protection of controlled waters in the vicinity of the site. These allow appropriate on-site pollution control measures to be designed.

It is important that the environmental ideas incorporated in to the design are passed on to the contractors at tender stage and then again at the pre-contract meetings.

Best management practice

- Consider the type of surface and groundwater control measures that are appropriate. Include surface and groundwater cutoff techniques and potential recharge

- Establish the types of soils and subsoils on site (for example clays or sand), to determine the most appropriate pollution mitigation measures

- Review the need and timing for consents and licences.

5.2.3   Contract

The tender document should recognises the need for water pollution prevention (and control) measures and good working practices identified during the planning and design stage. This will encourage and allow contractors to include water pollution control measures within the tendering process.

Carefully preparing the construction contract documents, including elements relating to the management of water pollution on construction sites, helps ensure that good practice is adopted (see Section 4).

Best management practice

- Include specific clauses relating to the control of water pollution

- Highlight potential risks relating to water pollution identified at the planning and design stage

- Include details of licences and consents in contract documents.

5.2.4   Site set-up

Taking time to examine the set-up and layout of the operational site before the start of construction work provides an ideal opportunity to include passive measures that reduce the potential for water pollution.

The overall design of the site layout, the location of offices, services and other facilities, security measures and plant operational areas should be substantially completed before mobilisation. All should address the potential for pollution generation. The design should ensure that stockpiling areas, storage areas, fuel stores, waste disposal points, refuelling areas etc are located where they are least likely to affect controlled waters.

Surface water entering construction sites from surrounding land should be intercepted and temporarily diverted around the work area. Likewise, watercourses flowing through the construction site should, where practicable, be temporarily diverted around the area or temporarily culverted through the site for the duration of construction. In cases where watercourses have important fish spawning reaches, the implications of temporarily culverting or diverting a stream will need to be considered.

Haul routes should be set up in such a way as to avoid pollution to water. The length of haul routes should be minimised, and the gradient reduced wherever possible. Bunded ditches on either side of the route can help prevent runoff of silt and oil into controlled waters. Figure 6.17 illustrates the impact of storm runoff on construction site activities.

Best management practice

- Provide temporary haul road bridges over watercourses to avoid vehicles fording streams

- Minimise the length of haul roads on the site; minimise the gradients of the haul roads

- Identify potential closed-system disposal routes such as discharge to sewer

- Construct temporary haul roads using permeable material, perhaps laid on geofabric

- Construct gullies/ditches adjacent to haul roads constructed with bunds or dams to reduce the drainage water velocity and allow sediments to settle before discharge to the drainage system

- Install effective wheel washes with dedicated drainage and pollutant collection sumps and interceptors

- Ensure all licences and consents are in place before starting work.

Bildem Civil Engineering Ltd

New Road

Site Procedure 1 – Pollution and damage control

Revision 0, issued 01/01/2000

Your attention is drawn to the following measures, included in our Site Safety Plan and Hazard Analysis, which will be observed on all areas of this contract.

Prevention measures

1. All foremen are to stress site pollution and damage sensitivity to their operatives, either in toolbox talks or directly on the site.

2. All small plant such as generators and pumps will be stood in drip trays capable of holding 110% of their tank contents.

3. All small plant shall be positioned as far as practicable from SSSIs or watercourses.

4. Site foremen or gangers in each section will visually inspect all items of plant every day.

5. All items of plant are to be monitored for leaks and drips while in operation, and drip trays are to be maintained and emptied at regular intervals.

6. All faulty items of plant will be removed from site.

7. Non-absorbent PVC booms will be set up permanently downstream of the works set at 45 degrees to the bank. In the event of an oil-type spillage, pads, granules or an absorbent boom will be deployed until the contamination has been removed.

8. The Environment Agency will be informed of ALL pollution incidents and actions taken. This will be undertaken by the works superintendent or his deputy.

Minor spillages

1. In areas not adjacent SSSIs sand shall be stockpiled at each location and used to soak up pollutants, then removed and disposed of in an agreed manner.

2. At the SSSI and watercourses, absorbent pads or booms, as recommended by the Environment Agency, will be used to clear up spillages. A boom and a stock of such pads will be maintained by each section foreman, who will be responsible for co-ordinating the required actions.

3. On blacktop surfacing, absorbent granules will be used to clear up spillages.

4. All mopped-up pollutants will be taken to the designated skips located at each of the main site compounds for disposal off site.

Page 1 of 2

Figure 5.2 *Site procedure 1 – pollution and damage control*

Major spillages

The following actions will be taken in the event of a breach and/or risk of major damage to blacktop, pollution to a watercourse or land drainage area, or fish-kill incident.

1. Immediately inform the Environment Agency and, if appropriate, the emergency services.

2. Prevent traffic and/or the general public from approaching.

3. Render every assistance to the Environment Agency and/or the emergency services as may be requested to mitigate damage and/or secure public safety.

4. With regard to land slope and the apparent flow direction of any water or potentially polluting materials from any breach, where necessary construct dam bunds with earth, board and/or sheeting to prevent and restrain such material from reaching the watercourses and/or flows inundating adjacent property.

5. Notwithstanding the above, where potentially polluting material or liquid has entered the watercourse, booms are to be used where possible, to retain and limit the extent/effect of such pollutants within the watercourse.

6. Please note that booms will be operated permanently on the main watercourses.

For Bildem Civil Engineering Ltd

[*signed by person responsible*]

I K Brunel
Project Manager

Circulation: all site staff

Figure 5.2   *Site procedure 1 – pollution and damage control (continued)*

Bildem Civil Engineering Ltd

New Road

Site Procedure 2 – Control of pollution, site signage

Revision 0, issued 01/01/2000

To assist in implementing Site Procedures 1, 5 and 6, the following site signs are to be erected at the locations noted below. These signs will be available from/issued by the stores. If these signs are unavailable when requested, temporary signs are to be made and erected in areas where work is in progress. The location of Sites of Special Scientific Interest (SSSIs) can be identified by reference to the Chief Engineer's Department in the main office.

1. At all SSSI locations

```
┌─────────────────────────────────┐
│                                  │
│                                  │
│              SSSI                │   ............  X = 150 mm
│                                  │
│                                  │
│            KEEP OUT              │   ............  X = 150 mm
│                                  │
│                                  │
│      By order Bildem Civil Engineering │   ............  X = 75 mm
└─────────────────────────────────┘
```

Colour: white on red

2. At all river crossings, accesses, security stations and work areas

```
┌─────────────────────────────────┐
│                                  │
│                                  │
│        PUT ALL LITTER            │   ............  X = 150 mm
│                                  │
│       IN BINS PROVIDED           │   ............  X = 150 mm
│                                  │
│                                  │
│      By order Bildem Civil Engineering │   ............  X = 75 mm
└─────────────────────────────────┘
```

Colour: black on yellow

Page 1 of 2

Figure 5.3 *Site procedure 2 – control of pollution, site signage*

3. At all river crossings and banks

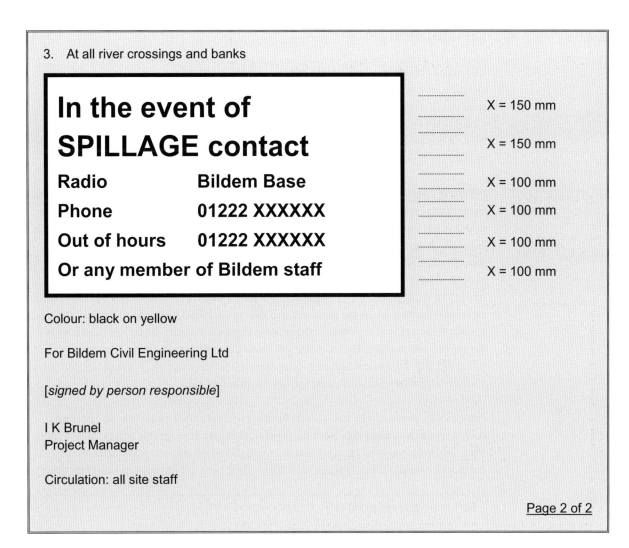

In the event of SPILLAGE contact

Radio	**Bildem Base**
Phone	**01222 XXXXXX**
Out of hours	**01222 XXXXXX**
Or any member of Bildem staff	

X = 150 mm
X = 150 mm
X = 100 mm
X = 100 mm
X = 100 mm
X = 100 mm

Colour: black on yellow

For Bildem Civil Engineering Ltd

[*signed by person responsible*]

I K Brunel
Project Manager

Circulation: all site staff

Page 2 of 2

Figure 5.3   *Site procedure 2 – control of pollution, site signage (continued)*

5.2.5   Mobilisation

The phasing of site mobilisation will ensure that those elements needed for support and for pollution control are included before the potentially polluting activities begin.

During mobilisation there are various methods by which the potential for water pollution can be reduced by planning and phasing. The site layout and operational set-up should have been pre-designed. The installation of temporary or even permanent services at the site at an early stage will offset the need for re-excavation towards the end of the construction life-cycle. Installing an adequately bunded fuel oil store, for example, should be an early priority, as should provision of security for the refuelling area during normal operations. Controlled delivery periods can help establish good working practices from the outset of construction. In addition, these measures will help make the site secure from theft or vandalism, which are common causes of pollution.

> **Best management practice**
>
> - Provide adequate training for construction site personnel
> - Wherever possible, developers should install equipment such as SUDS at the outset of a project in order that these may be employed to deal with construction site runoff. Thereafter, SUDS can be retained or modified as required as a permanent surface water treatment facility.

5.2.6 Construction

The actual construction processes and the various associated support service activities should each be assessed, after which working practices should be identified that will minimise the potential impacts on the aquatic environment.

Section 6 contains descriptions of typical site operations and the potential they have to pollute the aquatic environment. Methods of control and treatment are also included.

Adopting construction techniques that are sympathetic to the natural aquatic environment reduces the risk of water pollution. For example, concrete batched on site or delivered should be contained in order to minimise the risk of uncontrolled washings being discharged. Methods of on-site excavation for below-ground works and of site runoff and groundwater control should be selected so as to minimise discharge and to provide systems that allow treatment before discharge. The design of on-site traffic routes can make a positive contribution too. Large plant, particularly tracked, should travel in straight lines in the main site and turn at specified locations to prevent soil structure damage and to reduce sediment-contaminated runoff. Installing foundations during construction can lead to water pollution on construction sites – for example, piling disturbs the ground and may create pathways for pollution. Figure 6.18 illustrates a variety of uncontrolled discharges from construction sites.

Pollution incidents can be toxic, even from apparently minor sources such concrete delivery vehicles. Washings from these vehicles represent a serious source of pollution from construction sites. They are usually highly alkaline and corrosive and can have an immediate and significant impact on watercourses if no action is taken to isolate them.

Best management practice

- Avoid mass overburden stripping on the site; expose only that part of the site essential for operation

- If topsoil is to be stored, avoid constructing stockpiles more than 2 m high. This will ensure anaerobic conditions do not occur and that the soil will remain fertile and capable of being re-seeded. It will also be less susceptible to erosion

- Promote the travel of all tracked vehicles in straight lines wherever possible when moving around site. Encourage tracked vehicles to change direction at a limited number of locations, perhaps on prepared surfaces

- Avoid unnecessary slewing of tracked vehicles and turning of large site plant. This will avoid excessive soil structure damage and will reduce the amount of material available for entrainment in site water

- Place silt fences of geofabric or similar material around open or exposed ground and stockpiles.

5.2.7 Completion

The final stages of construction have significant potential for causing water pollution. Early consideration of the activities and the inclusion of control measures will limit this potential. During this phase it is possible that any polluted material that has accumulated during the construction process can be released into the environment.

Final-stage activities that carry a significant risk of polluting controlled waters include surface finishing of the ground, buildings and other installations, laying pavements, chemical treatment, painting and adding the final cosmetic touches to the ground, as well as the sequence in which these are carried out. The laying of the wearing course on highways and car parks means that the on-site drainage designed and installed for storm and foul water management will be open and operational, providing a major potential pollution pathway to the aquatic environment. By controlling the use of chemicals and managing activities such as topsoil placement or landscaping, pollution can be minimised. Topsoil temporarily dumped on a finished roadway before final placement may cause suspended solids to enter the storm drainage system. Other sites for such activities should be found or control measures put in place. Paint or treatment product waste and washings must not be allowed to enter the drainage system. The washing of finished highway surfaces or other built features to remove soil and other accumulated matter must be conducted in a manner that does not lead to pollution via surface water outfalls.

Best management practice

- Re-seed any exposed ground and stockpiles to stabilise the ground and reduce erosion and gullying of such features.

5.2.8 Demobilisation

Demobilisation of the construction site carries a high risk of causing water pollution. Removing temporary storage facilities and plant leaves the exposed ground open to gullying and erosion, which may result in pollutants being discharged into controlled waters (Figure 6.17). The cleaning of plant before removal may cause contamination, from particulate matter in runoff to oils, fuel spills and cleaning chemicals. These activities should be controlled and managed in as much detail as the construction project itself. Decommissioning fuel storage areas, septic tanks, decontamination units and mess facilities must be planned and dealt with in accordance with the CDM duty of care.

5.3 TRAINING

The evaluation of the risk and the design and adoption of pollution control measures are the first steps in any training programme. All site managers, supervisors, foremen and operatives should be made aware that only constant commitment, briefings and training will ensure that standards are maintained.

Long-term education will ultimately result in more environmentally appropriate working and operational procedures (see Case study 20). Even so, continual development and training in response to constantly changing environmental legislation is needed to ensure that complacency does not replace ignorance as the cause of environmental pollution incidents from construction sites. Pollution minimisation techniques and their operation, supported by the existence and operation of emergency procedures, should be included within the site induction and training scheme. If during the life of the project, site operations change and are updated, or if alternative methods are found to be more effective, then update sessions of the site induction/training programme must be held.

A major road scheme involved crossing numerous rivers and watercourses and working adjacent to SSSIs, SACs and environmentally sensitive areas. The scheme employed 5000 personnel, with up to 700 on site at any one time, many subcontractors and third parties. A fundamental component of the scheme was the education of the workforce with regard to the sites' sensitivity, working practices and procedures. Education of the environmentalists and ecologists in construction techniques was also important, enabling them to contribute to the development and understanding of procedures. The education of the workforce was carried out by:

- introducing senior site managers at an early stage to ensure intimate understanding and ownership. General procedures were developed early on and these were introduced into specific method statements by the managers directly responsible for the work

- providing the workforce with a site safety, security and environmental induction on arrival on site, followed by the procedures and toolbox talks. One series of such talks was given by an Environmental Agency representative with the aim of encouraging the workforce to take ownership of pollution prevention on site. To reinforce specific procedures, signs were put up in strategic places across the site

- office-based specialist environmentalists were introduced to construction processes, augmented with regular site visits

- regular monthly meetings between the Environment Agency, English Nature, ecological consultants, consultants and the relevant contractors ensured the two-way education continued and was updated as situations developed and changed.

5.4   COMMUNICATION AND MANAGEMENT

Effective communication is essential to bind the project cycle together. Measures to reduce water pollution adopted at the early stages of planning and design must be followed through systematically and communicated to contractors responsible for the later stages of construction, completion and demobilisation. This is particularly true of large projects involving multiple partners and numerous subcontractors. A breakdown in communication is frequently the root cause of pollution events.

Even with the best intentions, the process of communicating pollution control measures will not be successful unless it is formally structured. In addition, organisations frequently require a formal approach to demonstrate their environmental credentials to clients, regulators and the public. The section below shows several ways of achieving this accountability, as explained below.

5.4.1   Environmental management systems

Alongside other sectors, the construction industry is increasingly seeking to achieve certification to the ISO 14001 international standard. This can either be incorporated into an existing ISO 9001 framework, or implemented separately. A formal EMS can be operated on a company-wide basis and allows environmental targets to be developed, including those for reducing water pollution. It can also define particular channels of communication and procedures that should be followed to prevent water pollution incidents. In addition, a project quality plan or code of practice can be produced for each individual construction scheme which details site-specific environmental goals and work procedures. The EMS identifies key members of staff with responsibility for water pollution control and assigns documents to enable the system to be administered. In large companies it can be beneficial to develop a dedicated in-house environmental team.

5.4.2　The Construction (Design & Management) Regulations (CDM)

The Construction (Design and Management) Regulations 1994 impose a duty on designers to ensure that their designs are capable of being constructed, cleaned, maintained and demolished in a safe way (see Section 3.3.3). This means that designers are already required to include health and safety issues in the basic design criteria for a construction project. Although the CDM legal framework does not allow for the inclusion of environmental aspects, the same basic pattern of responsibility enables designers to consider the prevention of water pollution (as well as other environmental issues) as early as possible. This puts the emphasis on the initial design stages, to ensure that contractors do not encounter problems at the construction stage.

5.4.3　Duty of care

The Environmental Protection Act 1990 (EPA) and the Control of Substances Hazardous to Health Regulations 1988 (COSHH) are based on the "duty of care" principle. EPA uses the principle of liability to control the passage of waste through an industrial process to avoid its release into the environment. COSHH concentrates on the control of hazardous materials to avoid adverse impacts on human health. The implication of duty of care is that toxic materials are monitored and administered by an appropriate system each time they pass from one individual to another, or from one process to another.

6 Water management techniques

6.1 INTRODUCTION

This section describes briefly the types of site operations that may cause water pollution on construction sites and the techniques that can be used to manage and control water.

While careful planning and management can help to minimise water pollution, accidents and unforeseen events can and do occur. A short section on incident control and emergency procedures is included in Section 6.4. It must be stressed that incident control is not a tool for managing water pollution on construction sites. The contractor should plan ahead to ensure that these procedures can be implemented in an emergency and they should only be required in the event of an unforeseen incident or accident.

While some risks of water pollution can arise from almost all construction sites, other risks are site-specific. Consultants and contractors must be aware of the different sets of circumstances for each site and adopt an appropriate pollution prevention strategy.

The checklists below indicate important considerations for a variety of site types.

Some EA/SEPA/EHS pollution prevention guidelines (PPGs) are referenced in the following sections. A listing of all PPGs can be found in Section 9.

6.1.1 Works on a greenfield site

Greenfield sites generally present a lower risk of water pollution than brownfield sites. However, several activities need to be considered:

- site clearance/fencing
- topsoil stripping
- drainage
- earthworks
- piling
- concrete works
- dewatering.

6.1.2 Works on a brownfield site

Brownfield sites present a significant risk to water quality with possible contaminated land and residual pollutants, existing pipelines and sewers and the demolition of existing structures. The main activities associated with brownfield sites are:

- demolition/site clearance
- treatment of contaminated ground
- drainage
- earthworks
- piling
- concrete works
- dewatering.

Particular care should be exercised where dewatering of the ground is needed. Contaminated groundwaters may be mobilised, both on site and from neighbouring sites, and if recharge is involved the necessary agreements and approvals should be obtained. Similarly, when installing drains, sewers and other services there is a risk of creating new pathways that may result in the release of contaminated waters to surface or groundwaters (see Section 6.2.2).

6.1.3 Works on a demolition site

Activities associated with demolition works that may cause water pollution are:

- uncontrolled flows from existing uncleaned tanks/storage areas
- causing damage to existing live/redundant services such as water services, sewers and storm drains, and oil and fuel lines
- discarded containers
- runoff from demolition works entering watercourses
- dust from demolition works entering watercourses
- leakage from demolition plant and equipment.

6.1.4 Ground investigation works

Activities associated with ground investigation with the potential to pollute water are:

- percussion and auger boring
- rotary drilling
- excavation for inspection pits, trial pits and trenches
- grouting works
- installation of standpipes and piezometers.

6.1.5 Works in or adjacent to controlled waters

Works in or adjacent to watercourses or other controlled waters comprise all investigation and construction works, including ground investigation works (eg bore-holes and trial pits), excavations, concreting works and other construction activities.

During the construction period of any project, watercourses will be at risk of pollution from many sources, including (see Section 2.5.4):

- excavations – discharge of contaminated water into the watercourse
- preparation processes
- concreting – escape of concrete from the works
- chemicals – escape of hazardous chemicals stored on site
- plant and equipment – contamination by the escape of diesel oil or fuel from poorly maintained construction vehicles or by spillage on site
- cleaning
    — escape of contaminated water from cleaning operations
    — escape of caustic or acidic cleaning solution
- trenches and pipelines acting as conduits for contaminated water.

Site procedure 3 (Figure 6.1) details conditions to be observed and suitable emergency procedures for working in, over or adjacent to water.

Bildem Civil Engineering Ltd

New Road

Site Procedure 3 – Working over water

Revision 0, issued 01/01/2000

The following conditions apply when personnel are required to work over water.

1. Safety helmets are to be worn at all times.

2. Personnel are to be accompanied.

3. High-visibility lifejackets or buoyancy aids (with lights as necessary) are to be worn at ALL times.

4. Wellingtons/high boots/chest waders are NOT to be worn. Steel toe cap boots are to be worn.

5. Working areas are to be kept clean and tidy at ALL times. DO NOT create trip hazards.

6. Location of rescue equipment is to be known.

EMERGENCY PROCEDURE

If someone falls into water from a working place you should observe the following.

1. DO NOT PANIC.

2. Shout for help "MAN OVERBOARD – MAN OVERBOARD".

3. Once in the water, remain calm – your lifejacket will keep you afloat until you are rescued.

4. If you fall into mud DO NOT STRUGGLE, other than to keep your nose and mouth above the mud.

5. Where possible, throw a ring buoy (with a retrieval rope attached and the remote end secured) as near to the person in the water or the mud as possible without a risk of striking them

For Bildem Civil Engineering Ltd

[*signed by person responsible*]

I K Brunel
Project Manager

Circulation: all site staff, all sub-contractors, notice boards, resident engineer.

Figure 6.1   *Site procedure 3 – working over water*

6.1.6 Maintenance works

Maintenance works are associated with the operational phase of a project and can include a wide variety of activities in common with the construction phase:

- earthworks operations, including topsoil stripping and temporary site roads
- concreting
- pumping
- storage, use and disposal of chemicals
- delivery, refuelling, storage and disposal of oils and fuel
- cleaning
- repair and reinstatement
- resurfacing
- painting
- resealing
- movement and maintenance of plant and equipment.

6.1.7 Pipeline works

The activities associated with pipeline works are primarily associated with excavation and reinstatement. However, the nature of the liner used for the pipeline works can have a significant effect. The main construction activities that need to be considered are:

- fencing and site clearance
- topsoil stripping
- drainage excavation and pipe-laying
- river/stream crossing
- overpumping
- backfill and reinstatement
- water-pressure testing.

6.1.8 Bridgeworks

There is a wide range of site activities associated with works on bridges or other major structures. The main categories are:

- temporary works for groundwater exclusion
- deep and shallow excavations for foundations
- piling operations
- formwork and concreting operations
- backfilling and other earthworks operations
- waterproofing concrete surfaces
- grit-blasting and painting of steel surfaces
- drainage of substructures.

6.2   SITE OPERATIONS

This section of the guidance document contains information on the following issues.

1   Bridges – permanent and temporary

- temporary works
- excavations for foundations
- piling to foundations
- formwork and concreting operations
- waterproofing concrete surfaces
- backfilling structures and other earthworks operations
- drainage of substructure
- maintenance of structures over water.

2   Deep excavations – groundwater control

- physical barriers
  - sheet-piling
  - diaphragm walls
  - contiguous bored piling
  - vibrated beam wall
  - cutoff walls
  - grouting
- pumping control methods
  - surface pumping
  - shallow wellpoint pumping
  - deepwell pumping
  - porewater pressure relief
  - groundwater recharge
  - recharge trenches
  - recharge wells
  - recharge water
- compressed air
- ground freezing
- electro-osmosis.

3   Site operations – general

- demolition
- culverts permanent and temporary
- drainage blankets and vertical wick drains
- earthworks – cut-and-fill, mounding and embankments, soil re-spreading, storage and stripping
- ground investigation – archaeology, boreholes and test pits
- cleaning – air, metal, paint, shot, stone and water or stream jet
- cutting – air, metal, shot, stone and water jet
- oil or fuel – delivery, disposal, refuelling, storage drums and tanks
- plant – construction traffic over ground and over water
- works in or adjacent to watercourses
- demolition works

- plant maintenance
- drilling works
- piling works
- sewage pipeline works
- concrete production, transport and placement
  - site batching
  - transport of concrete on site
  - placing of concrete
- thrust-boring/pipejacking
- segmental shaft and segmental tunnel construction
- chemicals on site.

6.2.1 Bridges – permanent and temporary

Temporary works

Where structures have to be constructed adjacent to or in controlled waters, temporary works will be necessary to prevent the ingress of water into the areas to be excavated for bridge foundations.

These temporary works are usually take the form of a physical barrier, the nature of which depends on the particular site conditions. The barrier normally comprises steel sheet-piled cofferdams installed around the area to be excavated, or soil bunds placed to divert the watercourse away from the construction. For deeper excavations, generally in open water, caissons are usually sunk to the required foundation levels by excavating material from within the structure until the necessary depth is reached.

The construction of temporary works involves the use of plant and equipment that can cause water pollution during operation. Fuel and oil spillages can occur, so suitable measures should be put in place to prevent pollution. All plant and equipment should be refuelled and maintained away from the actual construction site at a location where proper control measures can be employed to deal with any spillages.

Excavations for foundations

Excavations from within the temporary works mostly involve working below the natural water table, and hence groundwater is encountered. In addition, water tends to seep into the excavations through the temporary physical barriers through lack of watertightness within the system and also as surface water runoff from cut slopes etc. Suitable methods need to be used to control the build-up of groundwater and surface water runoff within the excavated areas to prevent saturation and possible degradation of the foundation material. To control the build-up of groundwater in the areas being excavated, the area to be built upon should be isolated by digging grips and trenches around the perimeter with suitable falls to sumps that in turn are drained by pumping out the excess water. Grips and sumps should be lined with an impermeable membrane to prevent contamination of the groundwater.

Construction activities may cause the groundwater to become contaminated and therefore direct discharge to the watercourse by sump pumping should be avoided. Preferably, site runoff water and water pumped from the excavation should be discharged to stilling ponds, where it can be stored to allow any pollutants and suspended solids to be collected and the water quality monitored before discharge.

Piling to foundations

Generally, the installation of piled foundations will be carried out at or near existing ground level, depending on the site conditions prevailing, so excavations are relatively shallow. Where foundations are to be sited at a depth to prevent scour by the adjacent watercourse, then some form of physical barrier is required, as described previously, to prevent water entering the area to be piled. In most cases involving piling, a platform is needed for the pile-installation plant and equipment, which would need to be dewatered, mainly of surface water runoff, to maintain a serviceable area. Construction activities may cause the groundwater on site to become contaminated; again, it should not be pumped directly into the watercourse but should be discharged to settlement ponds.

Piling techniques can be divided into driven and cast-in-place piles. Driven piles, such as pre-cast concrete, steel H and sheet piles, offer little potential for water pollution other than that associated with the use of piling plant, for which the normal control measures for treating surface water runoff will suffice. Cast-in-place or bored piles, such as those installed by shell and auger, continuous flight auger and other techniques, involve the removal of the subsoil from the bore. This may lead to problems on a site that has known levels of contamination from previous use. Special precautions are required to deal with the contaminated soil and groundwater to prevent it discharging to the surface water drainage system. Surface water from such sites should be treated to remove pollutants before discharge into the controlled water. Contaminated soils may be treated on site subject to licensing or removed for disposed at authorised sites.

An added problem with bored piles is that they require concrete to be placed in the prepared holes. Bored piles can either be installed with a permanent steel lining or have temporary casing which is gradually withdrawn as the concrete level is advanced upwards. Unlined piles could result in pollutants associated with concrete contaminating the groundwater, especially if the subsoil is highly permeable.

Careful selection of pile type is thus required at the design stage for sites in or adjacent to watercourses to mitigate the potential problems that can cause water pollution.

Formwork and concreting operations

Formwork and shuttering, for use in forming concrete structures, should be designed so that all joints between panels achieve a good close fit. Alternatively, they should be sealed to prevent grout loss. This will reduce the risk of contamination of the ground by the constituent cementitious materials. Shutters should have any oil coatings and release agents applied in the factory where possible, as spillages can be more easily dealt with there. Shutter oil is often applied at the workplace and multiple pours with fast turnaround present a particular risk. It is important that a safe contained area is used and that any spillages are regularly cleaned up and disposed of correctly.

Wherever possible, concrete should be carefully placed by the use of a hydraulic pump to minimise the risk of concrete spillages, especially for operations over a watercourse. Ends of pump hoses should be secured by means of a rope during concreting over and adjacent to watercourses to prevent the discharge hose accidentally depositing concrete away from the pour site. If concrete is to be placed by means of skips, the opening gate of the delivery chute should be securely fastened by a lock chain to prevent accidental opening of the skip over water, especially if that would cause spillage during concrete placement manoeuvres.

At the delivery point either for pump-placed or skip-placed concrete, measures for preventing concrete spillage from truck mixers contaminating the ground and leaching out into the groundwater must be in place for all concreting operations. Washing out of truck mixers, concrete pumps, skips and other items of plant and equipment needing to be cleaned of concrete after use must only take place at a designated area, away from the watercourse. Compressors or generators used for connecting operations should be fitted with drip trays to collect fuel and oil spills that might otherwise contaminate the groundwater and lead to pollution of the watercourses.

Waterproofing concrete surfaces

Generally, the bridge structure is waterproofed using different materials depending on whether the surface is exposed or covered. Concrete surfaces of substructures that are buried and in contact with soil or backfill are treated with two to three coats of brush-applied bitumen emulsion. For this operation, the waterproofing material, generally kept in drums, should be stored away from the construction site and far from watercourses. When being applied to concrete surfaces at the construction site, great care must be taken when transporting the drums to avoid accidental spillages. When in use, the drums should be secured on firm ground and within a suitable containment tray to catch any spillage. Suitable protection should be laid on the ground to prevent waterproofing material contaminating the ground.

Waterproofing the exposed surfaces of the structure is carried out by saturation spraying of silanes to impregnate the surface of the concrete substrate. Silane damages the aquatic environment and its use should be tightly controlled. Generally, this operation should be undertaken when the weather is dry and fair, with no more than a light breeze.

Silane treatment is normally applied in two stages, allowing the first application to dry before applying the second coat. They are usually applied to the concrete by spraying only the concrete substructure, working from the lower levels upwards. For substructure concrete surfaces care must be taken that any silane runoff is prevented from seeping into the ground, which could lead to pollution of the watercourse.

When spraying silane on concrete surfaces of superstructures spanning watercourses, the watercourse below should be adequately protected, usually by containment. Care must be taken that silane aerosol does not drift onto the surface of the waterbody. Silane impregnation of deck soffits, deck edges and parapet plinths deamnds enclosure of the working area. Further guidance is provided in the PPG *Maintenance of structures over water* (due for publication early 2000).

Backfilling structures and other earthworks operations

On completion of the structure the excavations around foundations will be backfilled and compacted with acceptable material, usually back up to original ground levels. Sump pumping of the excavations has ceased at this stage. It is important therefore that the backfill material is free of any contaminants that may seep into the groundwater and cause pollution. This can be confirmed by testing the backfill material to be used before placement. Normal precautions should be taken during backfilling operations to prevent oil and fuel from plant contaminating the fill.

The backfilling of the structure will continue up to carriageway formation level, with the backfill material haunched into the general embankment fill, from the rear of the foundations at a slope of 1 in 1.5. The backfill for this operation will be imported granular, free-draining material. A back wall drainage system will be installed with a drainage outlet pipe generally placed above the high water level of the adjacent watercourse and running the whole length of the wall. Again this granular material must undergo testing to confirm that no contaminants are present, before backfilling operations.

Pollution of the groundwater can therefore virtually be eliminated by the correct choices of backfill material.

Drainage of substructure

As mentioned in the previous section, the substructure is provided with a positive drainage system, complete with rodding equipment, with the drainage outfall connected to a catchpit. Water from catchpits may be discharged to controlled waters subject to adequate pollution prevention measures and formal discharge consent, if appropriate.

Maintenance of structures over water

The maintenance of structures over water (for example bridges and jetties) can result in water pollution (see Case study 21). Cleaning and refinishing activities can generate particles of metal, old paint and cement in addition to liquid discharges of detergents, biocides and new paint. All these can fall directly into the watercourse below or can be contained in runoff from rain or washing activities.

Case study 21 ☹ *Discharge of detergent results in environmental damage*

Detergent was allowed to escape to a controlled water and form a foam wall 12 feet high, 50 feet wide and 70 feet long on a nearby lake. The company involved was charged under section 85(1) of WRA 1991. It pleaded guilty and was fined £4000.

Source: Environ Law Mgmt 10(6) Nov–Dec 1998

The impact of abrasive blasting, which produces large quantities of particles, can be minimised by the use of power-tool vacuum attachments. Slag-derived grits should not be used for blasting as they often contain high concentrations of heavy metals. All runoff from water cleaning methods should be contained and receive appropriate treatment. Where old paints containing lead are suspected, they should be analysed before removal. If lead is present then health and safety issues must be taken into account when the containment method is chosen. Primers or paints containing lead must not be re-applied.

If conventional spray painting systems are used incorrectly, large quantities of paint aerosol can drift onto waterbody surfaces or biota. Strict control should be kept of spraying activities and alternative methods of painting should be sought (for example brush or electrostatic spray unit). Similarly, care should be taken when concrete is applied using spray methods.

Primers containing 1,1,1 trichloroethane must not be used. If thinners are to be used, they should be mixed with the paint away from the waterbody. If epoxy or polyurethane resins are to be used, solvent-free or low-solvent products should be selected.

Pollution Prevention Guideline Note 23 covers the maintenance of structures over water, and may be obtained from the environmental agencies.

6.2.2   Deep excavations – groundwater control

When construction involves work within the natural water table, there is a risk that groundwater may already be contaminated because of activities previously carried out on site, especially on brownfield sites. In such circumstances, construction work could mobilise this pollutant, resulting in it being discharged to surface waters draining the site. Alternatively, the construction activities may cause groundwater on site to become contaminated and subsequently be discharged to watercourses draining the area.

This section will not address in detail the technical or engineering aspects of installation of groundwater control techniques. Details will be given of the pollution and groundwater control techniques relative to the set-up and day-to-day operation of a construction site. Site procedure 4 (Figure 6.2) gives an example of appropriate groundwater control methods and issues that should be raised with site staff.

Bildem Civil Engineering Ltd

New Road

Site Procedure 4
Temporary measures for the disposal of groundwater

Revision 0, issued 01/01/2000

Any groundwater that needs to be disposed of from excavations, catchpits or drainage runs etc can be dealt with by the following alternative means.

1. Water can be pumped out and allowed to disperse over the ground (other than land designated as SSSI) and allowed to percolate away naturally. This water MUST NOT be allowed to run off into any rivers, streams, carrier drains or land drains, or SSSIs.

2. Soakaways may be dug and water allowed to disperse naturally, again subject to preventing runoff directly into watercourses or SSSIs.

3. Water can be pumped into groundwater discharge stilling basins, as detailed on the attached drawing no 1234/Revision A. The water can then be allowed to evaporate. It should not be permitted to outfall into watercourses or SSSIs.

4. Water pumped into bowsers can be removed to disposal at agreed locations.

NOTE: Failure to observe these requirements could result in prosecution.

For Bildem Civil Engineering Ltd

[*signed by person responsible*]

I K Brunel
Project Manager

Circulation: all site staff.

Figure 6.2   *Site procedure 4 – temporary measures for the disposal of groundwater*

Groundwater at a construction site can be controlled by either or both of the following:

- water exclusion techniques by the installation of a physical barrier
- pumping control methods to lower the groundwater level.

The choice or combination of techniques will depend on the amount of dewatering required, the excavation depth relative to normal groundwater level, the nature of the surrounding ground and developments, and the nature of the ground and groundwater.

Pumping control methods cause drawdown of the surrounding groundwater. The extent of this is determined by the surrounding ground characteristics. In some cases drawdown may reach unacceptable levels and cause pollution problems in addition to the engineering ones. Such pollution problems may include:

- potential derogation of a local water supply well or existing groundwater control scheme
- the drainage of soft or loose soils into the excavation, creating disposal problems
- leaching of contaminants present in the local environment into the construction site
- saline intrusion where construction works are on or adjacent to a coastal site.

Physical barriers

The choice of groundwater exclusion technique depends on the requirements of each site. Considerations include the level of the groundwater relative to the excavation, superficial and solid geology characteristics, the nature of the groundwater, the sensitivity of the surrounding aquatic environment and the existing adjoining developments (see *Hydraulic measures for the control and treatment of groundwater pollution* [CIRIA R186, 1999]).

- **Sheet-piling** – steel sheet-piles driven or vibrated into the ground to provide a cutoff wall can be extremely effective (Figure 6.3). Problems are encountered when obstructions within the ground, either in the form of made ground or natural elements such as boulders, significantly decreases the effectiveness of the cutoff. Such obstructions may damage piles by toe deflection, clutch damage and pile separation. Failure of the pile driving on obstructions sometimes incurs great additional expense through the need to employ specialist diving contractors to examine and remove obstructions. Noise and/or vibration during installation can also cause problems. There several advantages to be gained from installing sheet-pile walls. The wall itself, with appropriate cantilever provision and/or propping, can support the soils around the construction site, reducing the need for additional space for earthworks, the volume of disturbed ground, the amount of earthworks and the need for slope battering within an excavation. A reduction in the quantity of material handled or disturbed during a construction project clearly has a favourable knock-on effect upon the volume of material available for entrainment within site water discharges.

- **Diaphragm walls** – concrete diaphragm walls can be installed in most types of ground from soils to relatively weak rock. These structural features, once installed, can often act as the below-ground side walls of the completed structure and be budgeted for not only on the basis of groundwater control but as part of the final construction cost (Figure 6.3).

- **Contiguous bored piling** – contiguous bored and interlocking (secant) piling can be used in a similar way to diaphragm walls and are generally less expensive for use as temporary works (Figure 6.3). Problems do occur with achieving a full seal between contiguous piles, however.

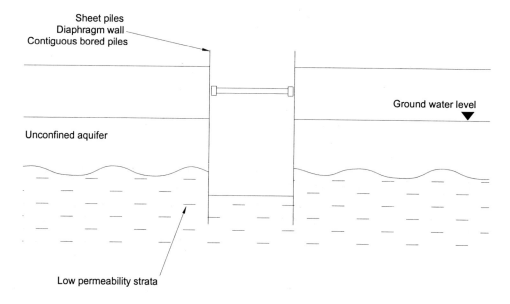

Figure 6.3 *Use of physical barriers – high-strength materials; general arrangement (based on CIRIA C515, 2000a)*

- **Vibrated beam wall** – vibrated beam wall cutoff measures involve the driving of an H-pile to the designed base of the cutoff structure within homogeneous soils comprising silts and/or sands. The pile is then withdrawn and grout injected via toe nozzles during withdrawal. The grout forms a thin, structurally weak but low-permeability membrane. The replacement membrane does not provide any structural support for the soils within the excavation and can only be effectively installed in homogeneous soils generally comprising sands and silts. If a slope within the construction excavation subsequently fails, it is likely to affect the operation of the cutoff feature, particularly if the failure plane occurred through the installed membrane. Thus the land area required for such a feature is high and the need for battering or staged excavation on a construction site exposes more of the ground to the threat of erosion, entrainment and subsequent pollution. The main advantage of this method is that it is relatively cheap to install (Figure 6.4).

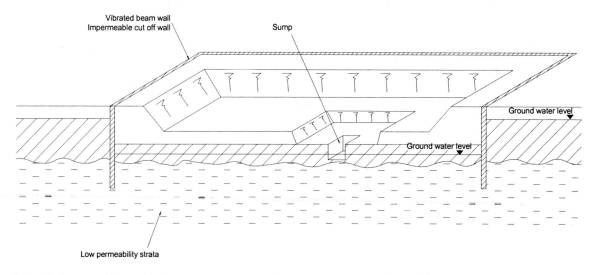

Figure 6.4 *Physical barrier – low-strength materials; general arrangement (based on CIRIA C515, 2000a)*

- **Cutoff walls** – low-permeability cutoff walls can be used to restrict water flow into open excavations. These are formed by effectively curtaining the site with a wall made of either bentonite slurry or natural clay. A shallow trench is generally easy and cheap to install so long as the ground in which the installation takes place is strong enough to stand the initial excavation or trench support equipment used. Costs quickly become prohibitive as depth increases. In certain cases the grout may itself become a source of pollution and can wash into the ground and surface water, especially if poorly mixed or installed.

- **Grouting** – grouting methods vary according to the requirement. The methods range from injection of cement-based grout to chemical/resin grouting used to fill the soil/rock voids, thus preventing water transmission. The equipment for cement-based grout application is relatively simple, easy to use and can be employed in tunnel construction where space is limited. Chemical grouting is also a method of water exclusion. Chemicals and/or resins are injected to form a solid, chemically bonded curtain. Jetting grout into forms a curtain of columns or sheets of soil/grout that overlap to form a cutoff. Problems with all these methods include incomplete treatment, with breaks in the grout or chemical curtains that potentially allow a significant water flow to remain. This may be very difficult to deal with if exposed during construction. Other problems include the possibility of the grouting itself polluting either groundwater or surface runoff (Figure 6.5).

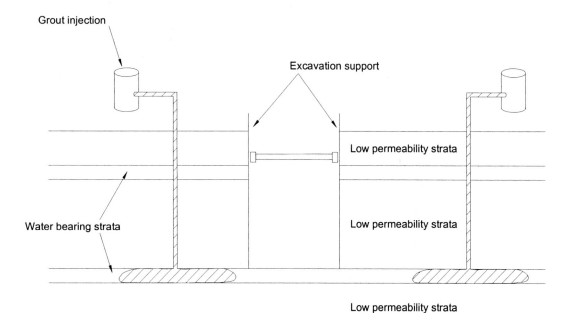

Figure 6.5   *Cutoff grouting used to restrict groundwater flow into construction excavations (based on CIRIA C515, 2000a)*

Pumping control methods

Management and control of groundwater within construction sites by the use of pumping involves the techniques set out below.

- **Surface pumping** – sump pumping and pumping from near-surface drainage pipes controls shallow groundwater or helps to prevent recharge of site groundwater by surface water. That is, it will prevent infiltration, for example via pumped French drains, and may be effective in controlling overbleed. Overbleed occurs when water is still present, even after a permeable stratum overlying an impermeable or relatively impermeable stratum has been dewatered. Any excavation into the impermeable stratum will allow leakage of that water at the permeable/impermeable boundary, which may cause instability and erosion. Sump pumping can be an effective and inexpensive method of controlling inflow of water into shallow excavations, especially in coarse-grained soils. However, it may not be sufficient to prevent seepage and potential instability on some cut slopes or faces in the construction excavation. These methods of pumping will not control groundwater at depth but may help to control pollution by reducing the level of groundwater to beneath the base of the construction site. This significantly reduces the potential for waterlogging and subsequent pollution runoff. These methods of shallow groundwater control are unlikely to be effective in reducing porewater pressures in fine-grained materials (Figure 6.6).

- **Shallow wellpoint pumping** – shallow wells and wellpoint pumping can be effective ways of controlling groundwater in shallow excavations on construction sites. Wellpoint installation is a relatively inexpensive method of groundwater control that, in single-stage installation, can achieve a drawdown of approximately 6 m in soils composed of fine sand to sandy gravel-sized material. The degree of drawdown achieved falls in soils with a higher content of fines, such as silts and clays. If hydraulic conductivity is high, for example in coarse materials, the installation and use of shallow pumped wells could prove more effective than wellpoint pumping. The filter zone installed for a shallow well can be more accurately defined during installation to provide more control over the rate of pumping and therefore drawdown (Figures 6.7 and 6.8).

- **Deepwell pumping** – deepwells are expensive but can control groundwater. Deepwell extraction systems usually require fewer extraction points. Extraction can be achieved by using submersible pumps to lift the water. The height through which the water needs to be lifted correlates directly to the size and power of the pump needed. In most applications, care must be taken that "snoring" of the pump does not occur. (Snoring occurs when the flow rate of water into the well is less than the pumping rate and the pump periodically operates in the dry.) During installation of such systems, close control over the well screen and filter zone can be achieved to target the extraction to the correct level in the well. A further development of the deepwell system is the use of additional vacuum lifting. The well filter is sealed, preventing air ingress and creating a vacuum. Thus, the negative pressure within the well continuously draws in water rather than relying on the inherent hydraulic continuity of the ground. Vacuum ejector wells are a variation on the deepwell system and, again within a sealed well casing, pump both air and water. This also creates a vacuum in the well. This method is suitable for use in fine-grained soils where flow rates are relatively low (Figure 6.9).

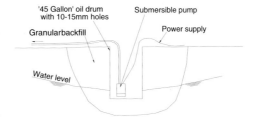

A) Perforated oil drum

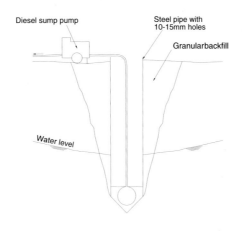

B) Perforated steel pipe
with driving point

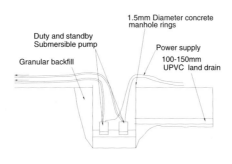

C) Concrete manhole rings
fed by french drain

Figure 6.6   *Schematic sections showing typical sumps (based on CIRIA C515, 2000a)*

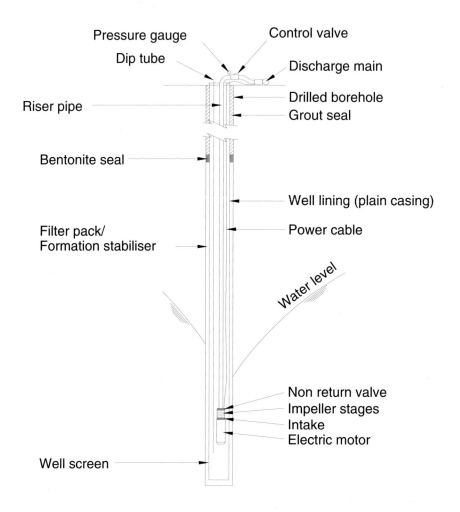

Pressure gauge

Control valve

Dip tube

Discharge main

Riser pipe

Drilled borehole

Grout seal

Bentonite seal

Well lining (plain casing)

Power cable

Filter pack/
Formation stabiliser

Water level

Non return valve

Impeller stages

Intake

Electric motor

Well screen

Figure 6.7   *Schematic sections showing details through well (based on CIRIA C515, 2000a)*

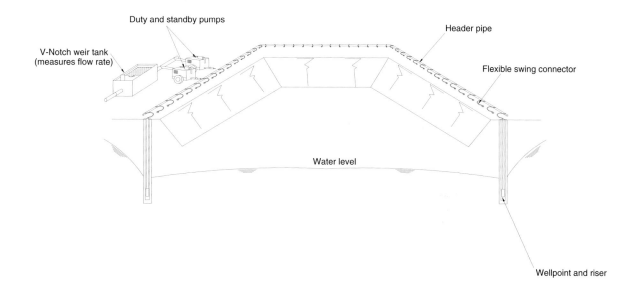

Figure 6.8   *Wellpoint system components used to control shallow groundwater during construction (based on CIRIA C515, 2000a)*

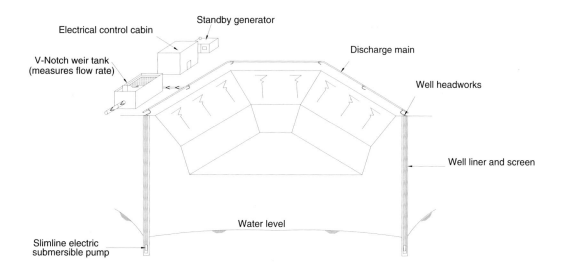

Figure 6.9   *Schematic section showing deepwell system components (based on CIRIA C515, 2000a)*

- **Porewater pressure relief** – the creation of a vertical flow path can be used to relieve porewater pressure in some cases – for example, from beneath the base of a construction site where the groundwater is confined below the permeable or near-permeable base of the excavation. The removal of the overburden during construction in such a situation can lead to mass or point failures in the integrity of the excavation base. This can cause release of water into the construction site with little or no control, and results in pollution. Should the use of passive groundwater control measures be employed at a construction site, sump-pumping plant should be provided to remove the released water off site (Figure 6.10).

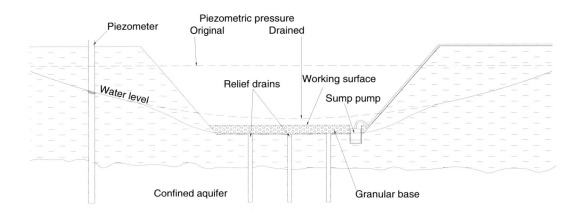

Figure 6.10   *Porewater pressure relief system to protect construction excavation (based on CIRIA C515, 2000a)*

- **Groundwater recharge** – when considering systems such as those described above in many cases it is necessary to assess the effect of dewatering on the surrounding ground and nearby structures. Recharging can mitigate the effect on the environs of the construction site. Waters removed as control measures on the construction site are recharged to ground around the site to restrict the actual drawdown to a narrow band of ground.

  Recharging is also a useful means of disposing of a volume of dewatered water, negating the need for additional treatment before discharge. Any recharge system will probably require consent to discharge from the relevant regulatory authority. Detailed site investigation information is required when designing recharge systems, as they tend to be affected by recirculation and clogging.

  If a recharge system is installed too close to the abstraction points relative to the hydraulic conductivity of the ground, recirculation increases. This requires a higher extraction flow rate to maintain the drawdown, which in turn demands a greater recharge rate and an increase in the extraction rate to compensate.

  To minimise recirculation, the distance required before recharge takes place can be between one and two times the distance of influence of the dewatering system from the site. This distance will be relative to the permeabilities of the stratum being dewatered and the required drawdown. In many situations, use of partial cutoff walls can solve the problem, because recharge outside the cutoff obviates the need to take account of recirculation. However, this method of groundwater control can be expensive.

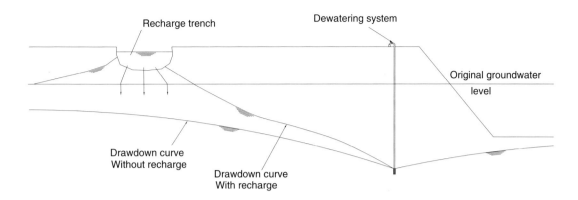

Figure 6.11   *Schematic section showing trench recharge system (based on CIRIA C515, 2000a)*

Recharge systems can take the form of trenches or wells or perhaps a combination of both.

- **Recharge trenches** – operate by allowing recharge back to groundwaters through the base of the trench. Recharge trenches are generally difficult to control because flows cannot be readily adjusted or stopped. Infiltration trenches are also prone to significant clogging during operation. If the base of the trench lies a significant distance above the normal standing groundwater level, the effect of the recharge may well be unpredictable (Figure 6.11).

- **Recharge wells** – can be designed and installed to allow recharging of the groundwater at specified depths and in a particular stratum. The control of flow into recharge wells through metered pipework can be accurate and readily adjusted to maintain continuous recharge water levels. As with recharge trenches, clogging can significantly affect the recharge well, especially if the recharge waters contain a high proportion of fines or colloidal materials. Generally, to allow the recharge to be maintained, each abstraction well should have at least two recharge wells. This allows one well to be closed down should maintenance be required to remove clogging (Figure 6.12).

- **Recharge water** – recharging can be carried out using clean water or mains supply water, but the chemical composition of this water may differ from that of the receiving water, and a licence may not be granted. The difference in chemical composition can result in chemical precipitation and subsequent clogging.

Case study 22 ☹   *Groundwater dewatering contaminates watercourse*

> While relining drinking water pipes, silty groundwater was pumped out of trenches and onto a road, from where it flowed into surface drains so that a controlled water was polluted. The company was fined £8000 with £1307 costs.
>
> *Source: Environ Law Mgmt 10(6) Nov–Dec 1998*

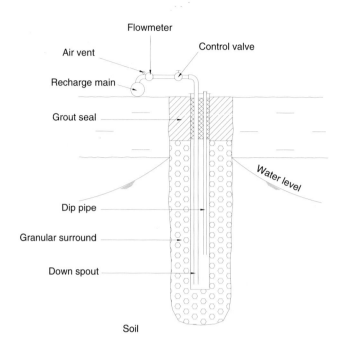

Figure 6.12   *Schematic section showing details through recharge well (based on CIRIA C515, 2000a)*

Compressed air

The use of compressed air is a well-known method of attempting to control groundwater inflow into an excavation. Typically used during tunnel construction, the sealing of the construction area from the normal atmospheric conditions allows compressed air to be used to increase the air pressure within the construction site. This reduces the hydraulic gradient and limits the inflow of groundwater. There are issues of cost and health and safety for construction workers with this type of system.

Ground freezing

Ground freezing is designed to provide a wall of frozen ground, and in some cases is used as a support for excavation. The ground conditions need to be suitable for the application of this method. Problems include potentially very expensive equipment and ground heave caused by freezing. A very low temperature discharge can result in thermal pollution of a watercourse, which can affect flora and fauna, particularly in the summer months (Figure 6.13).

Electro-osmosis

Electro-osmosis can be applied where an alternative control to ground freezing is required and can be used in very low permeability materials. The system creates a direct current running to the well screen, which acts as a cathode, from an installed anode (Figure 6.14). The effect is to generate a current flow that induces the flow of positively charges ions within both soils and waters. This causes movement of water to the cathode, whence it can be removed. The need for continuous power makes this a relatively expensive method of groundwater control, and there are health and safety considerations associated with electrification of the ground.

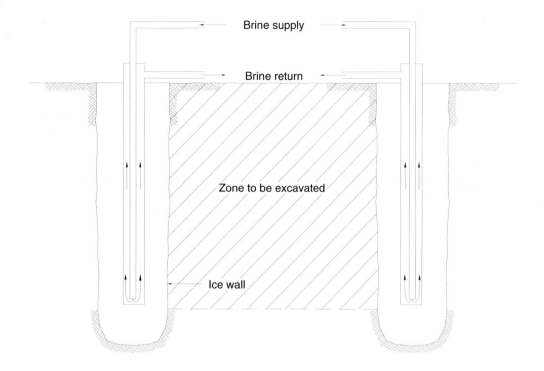

Figure 6.13   *Ground-freezing techniques to restrict groundwater flow into a construction excavation (based on CIRIA C515, 2000a)*

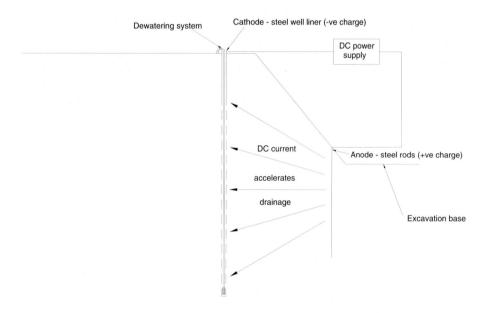

Figure 6.14   *Schematic section showing the principles of electro-osmosis (based on CIRIA C515, 2000a)*

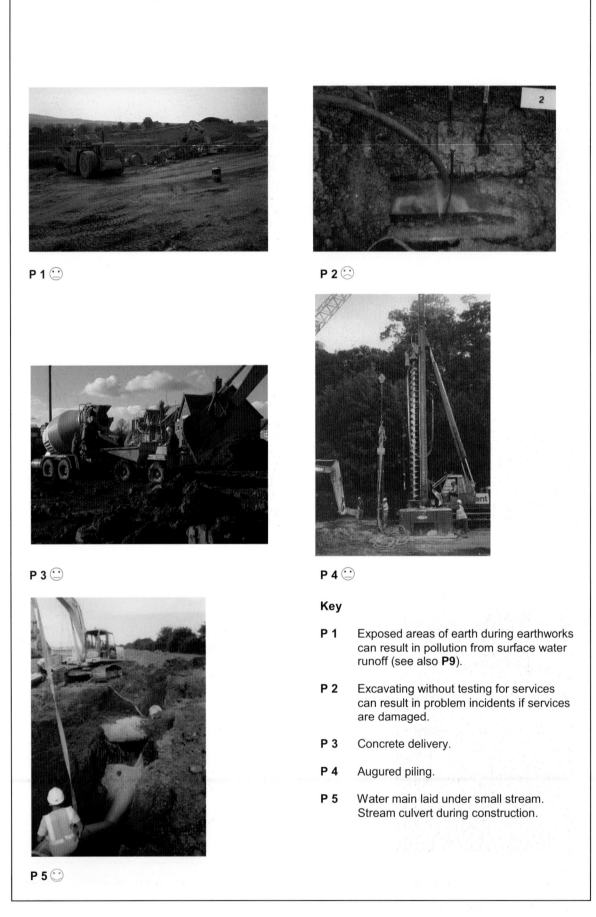

P 1 ☺

P 2 ☹

P 3 ☺

P 4 ☺

P 5 ☺

Key

P 1 Exposed areas of earth during earthworks can result in pollution from surface water runoff (see also **P9**).

P 2 Excavating without testing for services can result in problem incidents if services are damaged.

P 3 Concrete delivery.

P 4 Augured piling.

P 5 Water main laid under small stream. Stream culvert during construction.

Figure 6.15   *Photographs – site operations*

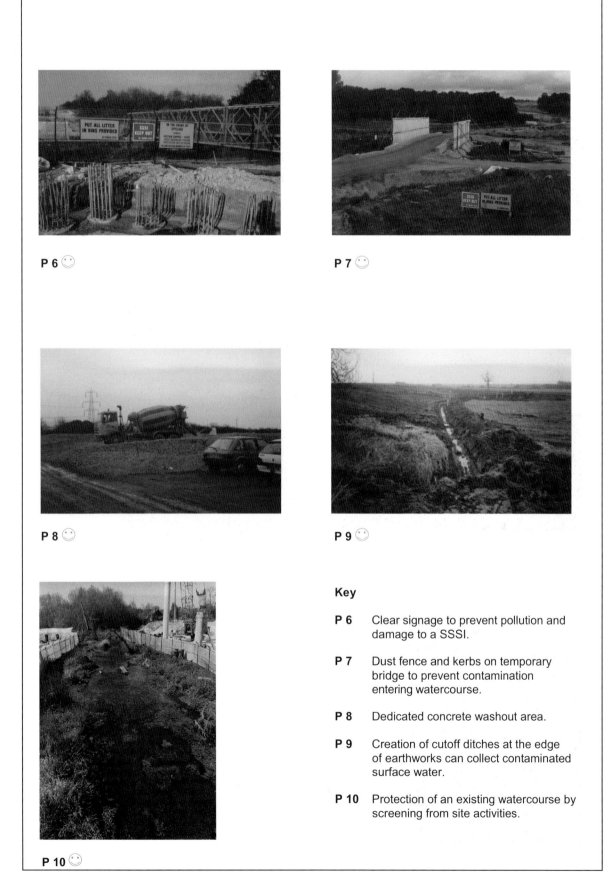

P 6 ☺

P 7 ☺

P 8 ☺

P 9 ☺

P 10 ☺

Key

P 6 Clear signage to prevent pollution and damage to a SSSI.

P 7 Dust fence and kerbs on temporary bridge to prevent contamination entering watercourse.

P 8 Dedicated concrete washout area.

P 9 Creation of cutoff ditches at the edge of earthworks can collect contaminated surface water.

P 10 Protection of an existing watercourse by screening from site activities.

Figure 6.16 *Photographs – mitigation*

P 11 🙂

P 12 🙁

P 13 🙂

P 14 🙁

Key

P 11 Earth/gravel bund and pumping during dry weather conditions provide some limited control of runoff from bridge works.

P 12 The pumping and earth/gravel bund, even with additional sand bags, provide insufficient control in wet conditions.

P 13 A sand bag dam works well to control water during wet conditions.

P 14 The volume of water during storm conditions is too great for one culvert alone.

Figure 6.17   *Photographs – working in wet weather*

P 15 ☹

P 16 ☹

P 17 ☹

P 18 ☺

Key

P 15 Direct discharge of silty water from a construction site to a watercourse.

P 16 Pumping out of excavations in an urban area. Silty water runs over the road and into the surface water drainage system.

P 17 Silty water discharged from a construction site enters into the storm water drains.

P18 Discharging water directly to land with landowner's consent and in discussion with environment regulator is acceptable providing water soaks away and does not run off.

P 19 Direct discharge from an excavation to a controlled watercourse without consent is illegal.

P 19 ☹

Figure 6.18   *Photographs – uncontrolled discharges*

P 20 ☹

P 21 ☹

P 22 ☹

P 23 ☹

Key

P 20 Suspended solids in watercourses are easy to identify and trace upstream.

P 21 Diesel oil contamination leached into excavations.

P 22 Concrete washout water entering a watercourse.

P 23 Oil contamination in temporary site ditches.

P 24 Poor site practice. Oils, chemicals and concrete will run off site and/or leach into ground in wet weather.

P 24 ☹

Figure 6.19   *Photographs – visible signs of pollution*

P 25 🙂

P 26 🙁

P 27 😐

P 28 🙁

Key

P 25 Temporary culverts sized to anticipate storm flows

P 26 Temporary culvert is insufficient to cater for storm flows.

P 27 Ad hoc approach to the management of surface water during construction. May be acceptable in dry weather conditions but will not work in wet weather conditions.

P 28 Poor control of surface water during construction results in site access roads becoming temporary watercourses. Straw bales have little effect.

P29 A temporary dam built downstream of the construction site in advance of any site work.

P 29 🙂

Figure 6.20   *Photographs – temporary works in a watercourse*

P 30 ☹

P 31 ☺

P 32 ☺

P 33 ☺

Key

P 30   Stripped soils and imported fill materials can generate dust in dry weather. This can blow away and enter watercourses.

P 31   Bowsers can be used to keep exposed earth damp and prevent dust generation.

P 32   Wheel-washes should be used at the site exit to clean vehicles before they leave the site for the public highway.

P 33   Road sweeping to keep road free from dirt and mud.

P 34   A poorly installed and maintained wheelwash can itself cause water pollution.

P 34 ☹

Figure 6.21   *Photographs – dust and dirt*

P 35 😟

P 36 😟

P 37 😟

P 38 😟

Key

P 35–39 illustrate bad practice examples of oil storage. None of these tanks has any viable containment for spills nor any security to prevent vandalism.

P 35 and **P 37** are not only bad with regard to potential oil spills, they also present a major health and safety risk.

P 39 😟

Figure 6.22   *Photographs – poor oil storage*

P 40 🙂

P 41 🙂

P 42 🙁

P 43 🙂

Key

P 40 Lockable fuel dispenser to prevent vandalism.

P 41 Portable and safe fuel dispenser.

P 42 Bad maintenance and no bunding result in leakage from a portable fuel tank.

P 43 Drip tray at a portable pump will contain any leaks.

P 44 Spillage from a portable pump will contaminate the ground.

P 44 🙁

Figure 6.23   *Photographs – oil tanks and pumps*

P 45 ☺

P 46 ☺

P 47 ☹

P 48 ☹

Key

P 45 Successful diversion of a stream at a new culvert.

P 46 Good practice in water control.

P 47 Uncontrolled working within a watercourse has resulted in a high suspended particle load.

P 48 Avoid plant working in the water if possible.

P 49 Excavation in watercourse results in heavy suspended particle contamination.

P 49 ☹

Figure 6.24   *Photographs – works in or near water*

P 50 ☺

P 51 ☹

P 52 ☹

P 53 ☺

Key

P 50 Temporary storage bund for oil and chemical storage.

P 51 Ad hoc temporary storage bund, poorly constructed and badly maintained.

P 52 Bund built around oil storage tank, but poorly maintained.

P 53 Temporary bunding for oil tanks. Maintenance will be required to ensure metal tank does not split or rust. Location of tanks close to site access road could cause accidents.

P 54 Oil and chemicals stored on ground with no protection.

P 54 ☹

Figure 6.25   *Photographs – storage and bunding*

P 55 ☹

P 56 😐

P 57 ☺

P 58 ☺

Key

P 55 Ad hoc use of a cattle trough as a settlement pond results in uncontrolled discharge.

P 56 Settlement tanks were required for dewatering operations. The volume of water was greater than the tank capacity resulting in the discharge of some contaminated water.

P 57 A well-constructed temporary pond with straw bale filter and oil boom.

P 58 A series of settlement ponds was required due to topographical constraints.

P 59 A temporary settlement pond becomes a permanent storage pond following construction.

P 59 ☺

Figure 6.26 *Photographs – ponds*

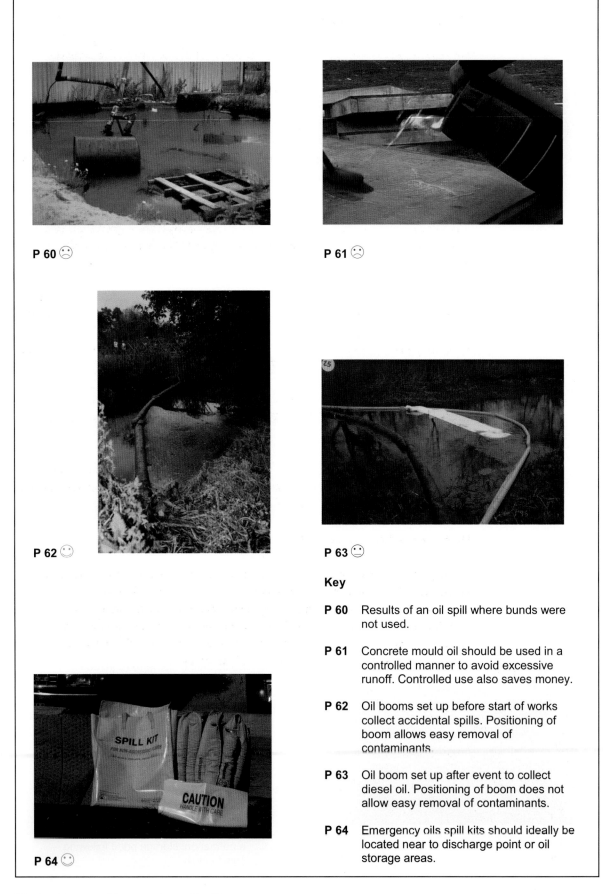

P 60 ☹

P 61 ☹

P 62 ☺

P 63 ☺

Key

P 60   Results of an oil spill where bunds were not used.

P 61   Concrete mould oil should be used in a controlled manner to avoid excessive runoff. Controlled use also saves money.

P 62   Oil booms set up before start of works collect accidental spills. Positioning of boom allows easy removal of contaminants.

P 63   Oil boom set up after event to collect diesel oil. Positioning of boom does not allow easy removal of contaminants.

P 64   Emergency oils spill kits should ideally be located near to discharge point or oil storage areas.

P 64 ☺

Figure 6.27   Photographs – oil spills

6.2.3 Site operations – general

Culverts, permanent and temporary

For ease of construction, permanent or temporary culverts are usually constructed along the line of the existing watercourse, or the existing watercourse is temporarily diverted. In the latter case, the new structure is built on the original line, with the watercourse being redirected through the new culvert. Alternatively, the culvert is constructed off-line of the existing watercourse and then the watercourse is diverted permanently through the new construction. Diversion of a watercourse, whether temporary or permanent, to enable construction, is usually restricted to streams and small rivers. In all regions of the UK, proposed river diversions must be discussed in advance with the environment regulator as consent for these works may be required. Permanent diversions of the watercourse have to satisfy the regulator's requirements that the natural ecology will not be impaired. Site procedure 8 (Figure 6.33) gives an example of how to control activities relating to stream diversions. Figure 6.20 illustrates temporary works within watercourses.

If consent is given for diversion of the watercourse, construction can take place with minimal risk of causing water pollution. Generally, culverts are constructed of pre-cast concrete pipes, corrugated steel pipes, or pre-cast concrete box sections for small to medium span ranges. For larger spans, multi-plate corrugated steel structures are used as well as *in situ* concrete construction, either box-section or portal frames.

If the watercourse is to be diverted back to its original line through the above types of structures then the construction site must be cleared of materials and substances that might lead to water pollution.

If culverts have to be constructed without the benefit of a diversion, this can lead to potential sources of ground contamination during construction similar to those outlined for bridges, hence it is essential to implement procedures to prevent water pollution.

Drainage blankets and vertical wick drains

Drainage blankets and vertical wick drains are frequently located close to the natural groundwater table and consequently there is a risk of pollution. Groundwater contamination can be prevented by pumping to lower the groundwater level or by installing a physical barrier. Operations including excavation and movement of earthworks, and import of granular fill material may require specific measures to be taken, as discussed in the relevant sections of this chapter.

Case study 23 ☺   *Crossing an environmentally important stream*

Construction of an 8.5 km pipeline across an area notable for the environmental importance of its network of ancient drainage ditches and streams required particular techniques at the stream crossings. Work was undertaken in the presence of representatives of environmental, conservation and drainage management bodies and an environment liaison officer appointed to the contract by the client.

The following technique was used on a narrow stream containing fast-flowing water. The natural clay in the area was used to form a bund upstream and downstream of the 2–3 m working width. It was found that a watertight seal could only be ensured if the vegetation and stream bed deposits were removed down to the underlying clay. The pipeline trench was excavated to at least 1 m below stream bed level. Excavated material was placed away from the stream edge to prevent materials or water runoff entering the stream outside the bunded area.

When the clay bunds were removed following infilling of the excavation, the flow of water was very high, resulting in little attenuation of suspended solids by the straw bale which had been placed downstream of the bund. The method was subsequently adapted to utilise a series of bales placed at regular intervals downstream to reduce the speed of water flow and the suspended solids.

Twenty minutes after completion of the work no visible impact on water quality could be observed. Water quality sampling was undertaken before and immediately after the pipeline installation.

Earthworks – cut-and-fill, mounding and embankments, soil re-spreading, storage and stripping

Construction works that disturb the original ground surface may potentially cause water pollution. In the context of a civil engineering project, earthworks involve excavating, storing, moving, importing, exporting and depositing various materials that carry varying risks of pollution depending upon the site's location (see Case study 24). The first operation is usually topsoil stripping, which should be followed by containment and treatment of site runoff. Minimising and phasing the exposure of ground before surfacing or grass seeding can reduce the scale of the treatment methods required.

The mobile nature of construction projects introduces some secondary effects caused by earthworks operations. These necessitate the inclusion of wheel-washers and dust-suppression measures to prevent the migration of pollutants.

The use of ponds, filter strips, swales and cutoff ditches and mounds is necessary if there is a risk of pollution. These measures are required not only in the immediate vicinity of the operation but also where topsoil or other excavated material is stockpiled. Earthworks operations next to a watercourse present a greater risk than those on sites which are far from water features. Where possible, permanent drainage works, such as top-of-batter cutoff drains or ditches, should be constructed as early as possible to divert surface water away from the earthworks operations. Protection and maintenance of the permanent drainage works is required throughout the contract.

Case study 24 ☹   *Infilling results in suspended sediment discharge*

While infilling of a reservoir took place, large quantities of sludge polluted 1.3 km of a brook. The company was fined £6000 with £1658 costs.

Source: Env Law Mgmt, 9(1) Jan–Feb 1997

Ground investigation – archaeology, boreholes and test pits

The pollution-prevention measures that can be taken during ground investigation works are similar to those for general earthworks operations, although the relatively small scale of the operations precludes the use of some techniques. Where groundwater from an excavation is not contaminated, infiltration methods can be used, including filter strips and beds and swales. Settlement ponds are also a possibility if the duration of the works is sufficient to allow any suspended solids to be removed.

Cleaning – air, metal, paint, shot, stone and water/stream jet

Site operations in which cleaning fluids, including oils and solvents are used, together with storage areas for these chemicals, need to be isolated by the use of impermeable membranes and bunding. Cleaning works that involve spraying, shot-blasting or other abrasive methods require the suppression of dust, which can be carried by the wind for considerable distances. Screening of the working area with plastic sheeting or damping down with a water spray is necessary. Further guidance can be found in PPG 13: *The use of high pressure water and steam cleaners*. Figure 6.21 illustrates construction site dust and dirt suppression measures and the consequences of not applying them.

Cutting – air, metal, shot, stone and water jet

Cutting operations utilise many substances that can result in water pollution. Cutting often requires significant volumes of water for lubrication or (in the case of water jet cutting) for the actual cutting process. Cutting fluids, oils and abrasives can become mixed with the water and distributed over a wide area. The runoff from the cutting works should be contained by bunding and the working area should be covered with an impermeable membrane if there is any risk of contaminating groundwater.

Dry blasting may generate large quantities of dust that can be carried by the wind for considerable distances. Screening of the working area with plastic sheeting is an effective method of mitigating any effects.

Oil or fuel – delivery, disposal, refuelling and storage drums and tanks

The fuel/oil transfer area should be located on an impermeable pavement with a bunding facility capable of handling a major spill during delivery and/or an adequately designed interceptor drainage system.

Storage of fuel and oil on sites and the procedures during delivery and transferring of fuel should be controlled. Site procedure 5 (Figure 6.30) gives an example of how to control refuelling activities on site. All tanks on site must be clearly marked and should only be used for the storage of the substance for which the tank was supplied or designed. Tanks should be placed only on firm and secure foundations. Other control and management features include adequate bunding of fuel stores, lockable valves and trigger delivery systems (Figures 6.28 and 6.29 and Case study 25). Joint CIRIA and Environment Agency guidance is available in *Concrete bunds for oil storage tanks* and *Masonry bunds for oil storage tanks*. More detailed information can be found in *Construction of bunds for oil storage tanks* (CIRIA R163, 1997a).

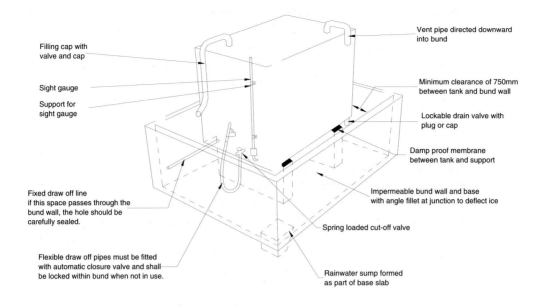

Figure 6.28   *Bunded oil tank (source: PPG2)*

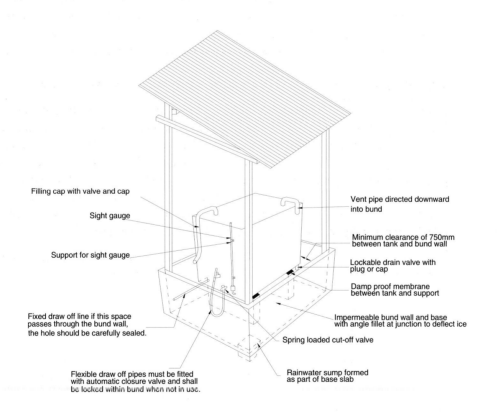

Figure 6.29   *Oil tank protected by roof (source: after PPG2)*

The storage of fuel above ground on a construction site must be carried out in such a manner as to minimise the risk of pollution entering controlled waters (Site procedures 6 and 7 – Figures 6.31 and 6.32). Every piece of equipment associated with the storage of fuel should be designed and installed to recognised standards such as BS codes or OFTEC standards (OCP2, 1995). All tanks should have bunds with a capacity of tank volume plus 10 per cent as a minimum, and steel tanks should be protected against corrosion. Equipment should be available to draw off water from within such tanks. All valves should be of steel construction to prevent frost damage, and the open and closed positions should be clearly marked. Rainwater should be removed using a pump (and the bund may incorporate a sump to facilitate this). The use of a valved outlet in the bund to allow rainwater to be drawn off without the need for pumping is not good practice as these may fail or be left open, making the bund totally ineffective. Publications such as PPG2: *Above ground oil storage tanks* cover other details, such as ensuring there is no direct connection between bunds and the on-site or off-site drainage system, pipework connection, vehicular collision protection, protection of tank sighting tubes, and minimum recommended spacing between the tanks and the bund base and walls.

In addition, guidance on recommended freeboard in bund designs is included in documents such as that given above. Freeboard is designed into tank protection systems to cope with maximum tank capacity, rainfall, allowance of 100 mm to accommodate fire-fighting foam, and a recommended 250 mm to cope with a possible surge caused by catastrophic failure of the tank. A puncture in a storage tank or storage drum can result in widespread oil or fuel contamination because of jet effects. The bund margin would need to be increased if this was considered a risk. Double-skinned tanks are in common use and minimise jetting. Figure 6.22 illustrates examples of poor oil/fuel storage facilities; Figure 6.23 shows a mixture of good and bad practice for oil pumps and tanks.

Case study 25 ⊗   *Drainage pipe renders bund useless and results in pollution*

Following public complaint, Environment Agency staff found a thick film of oil on a brook, which was traced back to premises where a leaking diesel tank was found. The tank had a bund, but this was rendered useless because there was a small drainage pipe in it. The tank stood on a bank around which was a brick wall where there were signs of oil seeping into the brook; the oil in the brook matched that in the tank. The site manager was aware of the leak but had not consulted the Environment Agency. The company was charged under section 85(1) and (6) of WRA 1991. Following a guilty plea they were charged £1000 in fines with costs.

Source: Environ Law Mgmt 10(3) Nov–Dec 1998

Bildem Civil Engineering Ltd

New Road

Site Procedure 5 – Fuelling procedures

Revision 0, issued 01/01/2000

1. Diesel will be delivered to plant on site in a delivery bowser dedicated to that purpose.

2. The driver or the supervising foreman will check the delivery bowser daily for leakage.

3. The bowser driver will be issued with, and will carry at all times, absorbent sheets and granules to collect any spillages that may accidentally occur.

4. Where the nozzle of the fuel pump cannot be placed into the tank of the machine to be filled, a funnel will always be used.

5. Each area of work shall have a designated fuelling area, which shall be as far as practicable from adjacent SSSIs or watercourses. Section foremen shall identify these areas to their plant operatives.

6. The central fuel tank will be stored in a bunded area and constructed on solid slab. The standing area adjacent to the tank shall be constructed with falls to an interceptor, before outfalling to the foul sewer.

7. Absorbent sheets and granules will be stored at the central fuelling location and be clearly signed.

8. All mobile plant such as excavators, dumpers and back hoe excavators shall be refuelled at least 20 m from any adjacent watercourse and, where practicable, off the blacktop surface. Large plant, such as cranes and piling rigs, will be tracked to the edge of their platform farthest from the watercourse before fuelling.

9. This procedure shall be issued to all site operatives, bowser drivers etc by their section foreman or controlling members of staff.

For Bildem Civil Engineering Ltd

[*signed by person responsible*]

I K Brunel
Project Manager

Circulation: all site staff.

Figure 6.30   *Site procedure 5 – fuelling procedures*

```
┌─────────────────────────────────────────────────────────────────────┐
│                                                                       │
│              Bildem Civil Engineering Ltd                             │
│                                                                       │
│                         New Road                                      │
│                                                                       │
│      Site Procedure 6 – Above-ground oil storage tanks                │
│                                                                       │
│                  Revision 0, issued 01/01/2000                        │
│                                                                       │
│                                                                       │
│   1.  All above-ground oil storage tanks must comply with the         │
│       attached guidelines issued by the Environment Agency            │
│       (PPG2 Above-ground oil storage tanks).                          │
│                                                                       │
│   2.  This is being adopted to minimise the risk of oil pollution     │
│       into surface or ground water, sewers or drainage.               │
│                                                                       │
│   3.  This procedure shall be applied by all section foremen,         │
│       and the installation shall be checked by the safety             │
│       adviser at the earliest opportunity.                            │
│                                                                       │
│                                                                       │
│   For Bildem Civil Engineering Ltd                                    │
│                                                                       │
│                                                                       │
│   [signed by person responsible]                                      │
│                                                                       │
│                                                                       │
│   I K Brunel                                                          │
│   Project Manager                                                     │
│                                                                       │
│   Circulation: all site staff.                                        │
│                                                                       │
└─────────────────────────────────────────────────────────────────────┘
```

Figure 6.31   *Site procedure 6 – above-ground oil storage tanks*

Bildem Civil Engineering Ltd

New Road

Site Procedure 7 – Operation of fuel bowser

Revision 0, issued 01/01/2000

In addition to Site Procedure 5, which covers pollution control measures in the fuelling of plant, the following procedure will apply to the management of the fuel supplied from the tank at the stores and the bowser distribution to the site.

1. The Main Stores staff will be responsible for dipping and monitoring the status of the tank in the main compound, and an order for gas oil will be placed as necessary.

2. When the delivery tanker arrives at the stores, no discharge will be allowed until it has been checked that the delivery is gas oil (ie "red diesel").

3. The tanker will dispense the delivery into the stock tank under the supervision of a member of Stores staff.

4. When the delivery is despatched, the tanker will produce a computer-generated docket that records the quantity delivered.

5. The bowser allocated to site distribution will withdraw gas oil as necessary, and the driver will record all quantities removed in a log book, which is kept in the bowser.

6. The bowser will fuel all plant, but will fuel hired plant and that of subcontractors only as directed by the general foreman.

7. The bowser will record all deliveries to site plant, including the following data: date, machine identification, quantity delivered and location.

8. The Bowser Daily Log will be submitted weekly to the Stores for monitoring and updating fuel usage.

For Bildem Civil Engineering Ltd

[*signed by person responsible*]

I K Brunel
Project Manager

Circulation: all site staff.

Figure 6.32   *Site procedure 7 – operation of fuel bowser*

Plant – construction traffic over ground and over water

Construction plant can cause water pollution by transporting and depositing fuels and oil, mud and contaminated material. Wheel washers and surfaced haul roads can prevent the deposition of contaminating material. Fuel leaks can be minimised by only using properly maintained plant, and the designated maintenance areas must be isolated from groundwater and watercourses. Drip trays should be kept available within these areas in case of equipment failure.

Works in or adjacent to watercourses

When undertaking excavations on river banks or adjacent to watercourses, excavated material should not be allowed to fall into the watercourse and so should not be stored or placed near the top of the bank. However, provided the sides of the excavations are sufficiently stable and there is adequate space between the excavation and the top of the bank, the excavated material may be used to form a bund around the excavation, to prevent flooding and pollution problems that might result from the flooding of excavations. Bunds to the tops of excavations will normally need to be lined to prevent erosion and contamination of watercourses by erosion of the bund. When undertaking excavation works in watercourses, a bund should be constructed around the works to protect them. The bund should be positioned to give suitable working area and lined with sand bags or other suitable material to prevent egress of water from the works area. Under no circumstances should water be allowed to escape directly from the site and enter a watercourse. If the works being undertaken are adjacent to a watercourse, then suitable means of catching any escaped water must be provided (such as cutoff ditches with chemical interceptors) to prevent unwanted materials from entering the watercourse. Figure 6.24 illustrates good and bad practices of working in or near water.

Where excavation works are to be undertaken either adjacent to, or in the bed of, the watercourse, and where water will need to be pumped from the excavations, settlement ponds should be provided. These allow sediment and suspended solids to settle out of solution before the water is released into the watercourse. Site areas designated for the storage and/or use of hazardous substances and chemicals should be protected by a bund surrounding the storage area to prevent the escape of any spilled substances into the site drainage system. The storage area should be provided with a temporary drainage system that remains separate from any general site drainage and cutoff ditches. It may also be necessary to provide an impermeable membrane overlaid with suitable fill in such storage areas to prevent contamination or pollution of the groundwater. The mebrane also reduces the possibility of pollutants leaching into watercourses in areas where the underlying stratum is impermeable.

The requirements for construction operations that have to be undertaken near or within watercourses (for example, construction of headwalls or outfalls) are generally covered under the sections for individual operations, such as for sheet piling. In general, the operations should be undertaken within bunded, dewatered areas, and in such a manner as to minimise the disturbance of the existing bed and banks of the watercourse. Where concreting works are to be undertaken, formwork joints should be adequately sealed so as to prevent leakage. The formwork structure as a whole should be sufficiently stable so that it is not displaced during the concrete placing operation.

No refuelling of construction plant should be undertaken while the vehicles are in or adjacent to watercourses, as this could lead to contamination of the watercourse through spillage of fuel. In addition, all construction vehicles entering the watercourse should be in good condition, and be provided with drip trays to prevent pollution through dripping of oil or fuel from the vehicle. The cleaning of all plant and tools should be controlled so that contaminated water does not pass directly into a watercourse (see Case study 26). The use of a designated washing-down area with a suitable drainage system to catch and contain all contaminated water ensures that contaminants are removed before discharge.

Case study 26 ☹ *Inadequate storage results in oil pollution*

More than 200 gallons of oil escaped to the Grand Union Canal because a tap on a tank was removed and the area was not sealed off with oil containers. There was also a history of minor spills on the site. The company was fined £7000.

Source: Environ Law Mgmt 9(1) Jan–Feb 1997

Where possible, all site cabins, containers, workshops, plant and storage tanks should be located outside the floodplain of the watercourse. Where this is not possible the site area will need to be protected by a bund to prevent pollution during flood conditions (see Case study 27). This bund should be additional to any measures taken to contain any chemical or fuel spills from storage areas.

Further guidance can be found in PPG1, *General guide to the prevention of pollution of controlled waters*, and PPG5, *Works in, near or liable to affect watercourses*. Site procedure 8 (Figure 6.33), "River and stream diversion", and Site procedure 9 (Figure 6.34) "Leptospirosis", highlight some of the environmental and health and safety issues relating to working in watercourses.

Case study 27 ☺ *Working in a watercourse*

A £3.5 million hydropower scheme in the Midlands involved working in a major river. The development was in a floodplain and mostly underground, which raised several design and construction issues. These issues were addressed in such a way as to minimise water pollution.

The main construction area was surrounded by an enclosed cofferdam bedded into adequate substrate to minimise groundwater ingress and of sufficient height to minimise flood over-topping of the cofferdam. However, through close consultation with the Environment Agency a temporary discharge consent was obtained for any water ingress during the construction phase.

A stilling pond was constructed from excavated material in an adjacent low-lying area to allow for the effective removal of sediment during the excavation stage. The correct design and utilisation of the stilling pond was essential to enable it to cope with large quantities of water pumped from the excavation during persistent periods of rainfall and consequent flooding. The pond produced water of good quality, which met all discharge consent requirements.

During the excavation period the material removed was stockpiled on site before removal and disposal. With the site being in the floodplain there were again issues about restricting flood flow. A stockpile layout was agreed with the local Environment Agency flood defence department to minimise this impact.

Bildem Civil Engineering Ltd

New Road

Site Procedure 8 – River and stream diversions

Revision 0, issued 01/01/2000

For each location where a river or stream diversion is required, a method statement **MUST** be produced and approved as stated in Site Procedure X *Method statements*.

The following points **MUST** be considered when writing the method statements.

1. Routes are to be based on the temporary Works Drawings 1234/1–8. Variations to these routes require consultation with the structures agent.

2. Cross- and long sections of diversions are to be based on Drawings 1234/30–33.

3. The diversion route is to be excavated while leaving a stank at each end, to allow a tie-in to the existing route in a single final operation.

4. The bed of each diversion is to be dressed with 70 mm of clean land-based gravels.

5. The Environment Agency MUST be given 7 days notice to inspect the diversion route before the act of diverting.

6. The Fish Rescue Service MUST be given 7 days notice of our intention to divert and the facility to rescue fish immediately following diversion and pumping out of the old course.

10. This contract is highly environmentally sensitive and the above procedure **MUST** be adhered to at all times.

For Bildem Civil Engineering Ltd

[*signed by person responsible*]

I K Brunel
Project Manager

Circulation: all site staff.

Figure 6.33   *Site procedure 8 – river and stream diversions*

Bildem Civil Engineering Ltd

New Road

Site Procedure 9 – Leptospirosis (Weil's disease)

Revision 0, issued 01/01/2000

Leptospirosis (Weil's disease) is an infection transmitted by rodents, especially rats, which excrete the bacteria in their urine.

If you are working in, near or on rivers, canals, sewers or any other place where rodents may be present – you may be AT RISK.

Infection usually enters through damaged skin or through the nose or mouth, and is especially liable to occur in damp conditions.

Before working in areas that may be infested with rodents ensure that:

1. Cuts, grazes and damaged skin are covered by waterproof plasters.
2. Wear wellingtons.
3. Wear rubber gloves.

At the end of the working shift, and before eating, drinking or smoking, wash all exposed skin with soap and water.

Personnel who think they may be working in the conditions described above should contact the Health and Safety Adviser for further information and guidance.

For Bildem Civil Engineering Ltd

[*signed by person responsible*]

I K Brunel
Project Manager

Circulation: all site staff, all sub-contractors, notice boards, resident engineer.

Figure 6.34   *Site procedure 9 – Leptospirosis (Weil's disease)*

Demolition works

While carrying out demolition works to existing structures, water pollution may arise from several sources (see Case study 28). Uncontrolled flows from existing uncleaned tanks or storage areas, together with existing live or redundant services – that is water services, sewers and storm drains, oil and fuel lines – should be controlled during any demolition works. Runoff and dust from demolition works should not be allowed to enter watercourses. Discarded containers and leakage from demolition plant and equipment also represent a significant water pollution risk.

Careful planning and thorough site investigation before the main works begin can significantly eliminate these risks. As with all demolition works, however, a competent person must strictly supervise the works to recognise, evaluate and deal with any previously unforeseen risks. Such risks include uncharted services, uncovering of unexpected materials/contaminated ground. The supervisor should also ensure that all previously established and agreed procedures are implemented on site. Further guidance can be found in PPG6: *Working at demolition and construction sites*.

Case study 28 ⊗   *Inadequate control during demolition results in severe oil pollution*

> While demolishing a building a company allowed a ball and chain to smash into a tank containing heavy fuel oil, which resulted in four miles of a river being polluted. The river is an SSSI, and the RSPCA had to launch a major rescue operation for swans and geese contaminated by oil. The company pleaded guilty to charges under section 85(1) of WRA 1991 and was fined £25 000 with £2890 costs.
>
> *Source: Env Law Mgmt, 9(2) Mar–Apr 1997*

Plant maintenance

Poorly maintained plant and machinery not only has a high risk of creating water pollution and safety hazards, it also brings economic disadvantages. Poor maintenance should not be tolerated on site. It is a requirement that all plant operators inspect their machines at least daily for mechanical defects and that a written record of inspection is carried out weekly. Any leakage of fuel, engine/gear/hydraulic oil or brake fluid should be reported immediately. Even if it is safe to do so, continued use of the machine should be permitted only if the flow of fluid can be contained (ie with drip trays or temporary repairs) and if either repair or replacement is carried out as soon as possible. In all other cases, machines should be kept away from environmentally sensitive areas and the leakage contained until the equipment can be repaired.

Contamination of ground or watercourses can occur while routine maintenance or repairs are being carried out. This generally results from the operatives or plant-fitter being ignorant of the site's environmental requirements. To prevent this, it is important that the following topics are covered in their site induction:

- works to be carried out wherever possible away from any areas at risk, preferably on hardstandings at the site compound
- emergency clean-up procedures and location of clean-up equipment
- re-inspection and, if necessary, cleaning of the area following completion of the works and immediately after the item of plant has been moved.

Further guidance can be found in PPG8: *Safe storage and disposal of used oils*.

Drilling works

Drilling equipment on site can vary from small hand-held electric or compressed-air drills, to lorry- and track-mounted diamond core rigs used in ground investigation works. Generally, water pollution occurs when the drill-flushings and drilling fluids are not controlled and come into contact with a watercourse. Fluids need to be contained and handled according to their contaminants. Airborne dust also needs to be contained and prevented from blowing/washing into watercourses.

Pollution can also occur from the drilling plant, service vehicles and storage containers. Strict supervision of drilling contractors may be required to ensure that fuel, oil and chemical spills do not occur and that emergency procedures are in place and are followed should there be a spill. Ground investigation drilling is often carried out in advance of main works in isolated areas and is particularly susceptible to vandalism. Special security measures may need to be taken to avoid such risks.

Piling works

There is a wide variety of piling techniques and pile types. Piles may be pre-cast concrete or steel, driven or cast *in situ*, bored or augured, or a combination – driven steel or concrete casing with concrete infill.

Water pollution may arise from any of the following causes:

- damage to existing services either from direct driving or drilling through pipes, by lateral pressure from driving adjacent to pipes, or from the weight of heavy piling plant travelling above
- contamination of groundwater by drilling muds and concrete if used while boring piles through permeable materials
- surface water contamination caused by uncontrolled runoff from site – especially significant where bored/augured piles are being installed and where drilling muds and high slump concrete are being used
- surface water contamination caused by drilling mud supply pipe bursts and leaks from drilling mud mixing and recycling plant
- leakages from piling plant, service vehicles and fuel, oil and chemical storage tanks.

Many of the above risks may be eliminated or significantly reduced by carefully assessing the works required and selecting the most suitable piling technique for the conditions. This demands the use of cased or driven piles in permeable ground, and driven piles where runoff may be difficult to control and where contamination may be high risk, such as adjacent to main rivers. The selection of piling technique to be used must always be costed against alternatives, however, and the cost of the environmental protection should be included in the assessment of the overall costs.

In addition to the selection of the most suitable method, extensive planning and site investigation is required to assess all risks and produce procedures for the reduction of such risks. These would include the provision of adequate protection for services, regular clean-up of arisings, designated disposal areas, installation of runoff control measures, bunding of drilling mud mixing plants and material storage areas, and the production of emergency procedures.

Piling contractors should be strictly supervised to ensure they adhere to agreed procedures, maintain plant and equipment effectively, carry out regular environmental inspections of the works and monitor water quality within nearby watercourses. At operative level, contractors should be aware of emergency procedures should a pollution incident occur.

Sewage pipeline works

Working with live sewage pipelines for relaying, lining, diverting, repairing or connecting new works poses a great risk of pollution, which is often caused by:

- inadequate pumps selected for overpumping
- inadequate flume pipe selected for flume diversion
- inadequate emergency procedures to cover pump breakdowns and blockages
- insufficient supervision of operation and monitoring of watercourses
- works carried out during periods of adverse weather
- the loss of chemicals and biocides used in re-lining operations to the ground and pipeline bench.

Careful planing and programming of the works and thorough investigation before works begin can significantly reduce these risks. Peak flow rates should be obtained and pumps and size of flume pipe selected accordingly. Long-range weather forecasts should be consulted and weather conditions assessed up until the works begin. The works should be reprogrammed to avoid inclement weather. Extensive emergency procedures to cover all possible variations of breakdowns/blocked pumps/pipes must be produced to include:

- standby pumps, suction and delivery lines
- emergency overflow ditches and pipes
- standby power source, if electric pumps are used, or standby diesel pumps
- a suitable method for switching pumps and lines, especially for out-of-hours works
- 24-hour emergency call-out numbers for pump supplier's fitters; terms and conditions of call-out to be agreed.

Where re-lining works are undertaken on pipelines which are known to be defective, the location of known leaks should be studied to identify potentially sensitive watercourses or groundwater which might be affected if the pipeline trench were to act as a conduit.

If pipelines are to be pressure-tested with water it is prudent to consider from where the test water is to be obtained and, after the test, where disposed of (see Case study 29). Consents or authorisations may be required for both operations.

All overpumping must always be supervised by competent people. Large-scale overpumping requires the provision of full-time pump men with 24-hour coverage and regular maintenance of pumps included within the pump hire contract. Emergency procedures to be carried out in the event of spillage occurring should be drawn up and kept available at the location of the overpumping. All necessary clean-up equipment should be available at the location.

Case study 29 ☹   *Inadequate sewer sealing procedure results in pollution*

In March 1999 a company responsible for relining a sewer with polyester lining containing a thermosetting resin was fined £5000 plus £1800 costs for polluting a stream with styrene. The spillage of heated water under pressure occurred due to poor sealing of the sewer undergoing treatment and escaped to controlled waters via a surface water outfall. The substance was shown to be harmful to aquatic life. The case was brought under S85 of WRA 1991

Source: Environment Agency

Other pipelines

The same factors need to be considered for other pipelines as for sewers depending upon the nature of the materials carried in the pipelines. The more hazardous the material (petrochemical products, fuel oils etc), the greater the risk. Gas pipelines contain liquid and solid residues that need to be dealt with when maintenance work is undertaken.

Concrete production, transport and placement

To prevent water pollution on construction sites it is imperative that the production, transport and placement of all cementitious materials is strictly planned and supervised.

1. **Site batching** – production operations vary in size from fully automated concrete batching plants on large civil engineering contracts such as airport runways and motorways to hand-mixing of mortar on small building jobs. Regardless of the size of the operation, the aim should be to prevent cementitious material from entering any aquatic environment. This risk can be significantly reduced by:

    *   using ready-mixed suppliers where the environmental risks of site batching and costs of associated environmental protection measures required are high

    *   on smaller sites attempting to mix concrete/cement in a single location

    *   containing all washout water and spillage with impermeable material

    *   controlling the flow of washout water by channelling it to settlement/filter tanks or ponds (Figure 6.35)

    *   discharging settlement/filter tank outlets into outfalls agreed with the regulatory body, preferably sewer or storm drains to reduce the overall pH of the discharge before outfall into any controlled water

    *   monitoring and testing discharges to regulatory body requirements

    *   locating the batching/mixing area and storage of constituent materials with due regard to site runoff, storm conditions and river floodplains.

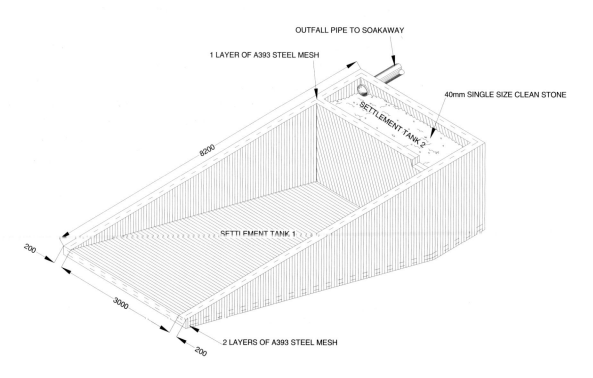

Figure 6.35   *Site concrete batcher sedimentation tank*

2. **Transport of concrete on site** – concrete can be transported on site by various methods, such as truck mixers, tipper wagons, site dumpers, machine buckets and concrete skips. The risks of pollution may be reduced by the following:

    - where possible, site transport vehicles should be washed out at the batching plant. The washing-down area should be contained and washings channelled into a batcher washings treatment facility

    - should no controlled washings treatment facility exist, then local washing-down areas should be created. These should preferably take the form of a steel skip or tank into which truck mixers can wash out. The contents need to be emptied regularly when settled. The washing of machine buckets, dumpers, skips and small tools should also be carried out in local contained areas

    - all approved washing areas should be signed; site labour should be informed of locations of approved washing areas during induction training and delivery drivers should be informed when they first visit the site

    - all loads need to be managed so as to avoid spillage while in transport. Load sizes must be assessed with regard for the type of vehicle being used, the slump of the concrete being transported and the ground conditions over which the load is travelling

    - in high-risk areas, such as those adjacent to controlled waters, extra care should be taken in designing, constructing and maintaining site roads and crossing points. Reduced speed limits may be required.

3. **Placing of concrete** – there are innumerable variations in the methods and locations in which concrete can be placed on site. To prevent pollution it is important that all concrete pours are planned and that special procedures are adopted where there may be a risk of surface or groundwater contamination. These may include:

    - washing-out of plant and equipment in agreed controlled wash-out areas

    - preventing grout loss from shuttered pours

    - reducing the amount of concreting above or adjacent to watercourses by investigating alternative construction techniques (for example, pre-cast or permanent formwork)

    - where possible, preventing concrete skips, concrete pumps and machine buckets from slewing over water while placing concrete

    - ensuring that excavations are sufficiently dewatered before concreting begins and that dewatering continues while concrete sets. However, care must be taken to isolate fresh concrete from the dewatered ground as grout can be drawn out and through the dewatering system, particularly with high slump concrete

    - ensuring that covers are available for freshly placed concrete to avoid the surface washing away in heavy rain

    - disposing of surplus concrete after completion of a pour in agreed suitable locations.

Thrust-boring and pipejacking

Thrust-boring and pipejacking are trenchless techniques for installing underground pipelines, ducts and culverts. They consist of using powerful hydraulic jacks to advance specially designed pipes through the ground behind a jacking shield. Excavation at the face is achieved either by mechanical means (microtunnelling/tunnelling machine) or by hand excavation. The jacks are located within a jacking pit generally on the downstream end of the pipe-run, and pipes are jacked towards a reception pit on the upstream end. It is essential that a comprehensive ground investigation be carried out to ensure that ground conditions are suitable for these methods of construction. The potential risks of water pollution with these methods are:

- **bentonite contamination** – bentonite is used while jacking is in progress to form a slip coating to the pipes to reduce the friction of the existing ground. It is injected into the annulus around the pipes either through the shield or through holes in the walls of the pipe. Experienced operatives will know when excessive bentonite is being used and possibly escaping through the ground. Regular monitoring of all watercourses should be carried out while works are in progress

- **grout contamination** – grout is used on completion of the installation to finally seal the annulus around the pipes and to fill any overbreak. Experienced operatives will know when excessive grout is being used and possibly escaping through the ground. Regular monitoring of all watercourses should be carried out while works are in progress

- **groundwater** – any groundwater encountered flows into the pit at the excavation face. Inevitably this water becomes contaminated with silt. This water then flows down the pipe to the thrust pit, from where it should be pumped to settlement tanks or lagoons, before outfall at agreed discharge locations

- **leakage from plant and machinery** – good maintenance and regular inspection of equipment is required. Clean-up equipment should be readily available and operatives should be aware of clean-up procedures.

Segmental shaft and segmental tunnel construction

These techniques involve the use of pre-cast concrete segmental sections installed to form the walls of the tunnel or shaft following excavation at the tunnel face or shaft bottom. The risks to water pollution are generally the same as for deep excavations, but with additional risk of contamination from grout. Grout is used to fill any overbreak on the outside of the pre-cast concrete sections and could cause problems if the ground is permeable or if passages leading to a watercourse are present. Even if ground conditions seem ideal, constant monitoring of all watercourses in the vicinity should be carried out while works are in progress.

Chemicals on site

The COSHH Regulations and the Management of Health and Safety at Work Regulations control the use and storage of hazardous substances on site. The duty of care principle cited in EPA 1990 (S34) applies to the management of chemicals on site. To comply with the regulations, COSHH assessments need to be made for all substances on site and measures produced to prevent or control exposure. Figure 6.25 illustrates good and bad examples of storage and bunding.

In complying with the above requirements, potential water pollution from substances used should be prevented by working in accordance with the control measures adopted.

Control measures may include the following:

- substitution of hazardous substances with safer alternatives, such as water-based products for volatile organic solvents

- using the substance in an alternative form, for example as a paste instead of a liquid or powder

- changing work methods so as to prevent the production or release of contaminants, for example by using spray application as opposed to pour-on

- enclosing the process or handling system as far as reasonably practicable, for example spraying inside sheeted areas

- using the substance away from high-risk areas, for example not oiling shutters above or adjacent to watercourses

- limiting the quantity of substances at the workplace to reduce impact should spills occur, for example using smaller drums

- ensuring that all substances are stored in suitable undamaged containers that are clearly marked

- wherever possible, keeping substances in a central, controlled, suitable storage area in accordance with the manufacturer's instructions and COSHH assessment recommendations. This storage area should prevent damage to containers by any means (such as machines or vandalism), prevent the unauthorised use of materials (responsible person to sign materials in and out), contain spillage of any substance (by the use of concrete floor and walls, and steel containers) and separate any materials that may become a hazard if combined (see Case study 30)

- returning all unused materials, spent containers, contaminated clothing, rags and tools to the stores for correct disposal

- producing emergency clean-up procedures for all substances used

- briefing operatives in control of substances and informing them of all control measures and locations of clean-up equipment.

The Environment Agency has produced the following guidelines for the prevention of pollution by chemicals, solvents and oils and for the treatment of spills:

- *River pollution and how to avoid it*

- *Chemical pollution and how to avoid it*

- *Solvent pollution and how to avoid it*

- *Silt pollution and how to avoid it*

- *Follow the oil care code*

- *Oil care at work.*

Case study 30 ☹   *Poorly stored chemicals result in fish kill*

Two hundred litres of chemicals escaped because of an incorrectly sealed valve, with a fish kill of 100. The company involved was charged under section 85(1) of WRA 1991; following a guilty plea, it was fined £5000 with £2500 costs.

Source: Env Law Mgmt 10(3) May–Jun 1998

6.3 WATER TREATMENT AND CONTROL TECHNIQUES

This section discusses:

general techniques

- waste – storage and disposal
- sewage discharges

techniques for the control of surface water

- oil separators
- ponds and lagoons
- retention time
- storage volume
- swale design – worked example
- infiltration basins
- filter strips
- filter beds and drains
- sedimentation tanks
- dynamic separator
- biofiltration techniques.

6.3.1 General comment

The techniques available for the control of water pollution are described below. Table 6.1 shows a matrix of the more common discharge treatment techniques and the pollutants that are treated by them.

Table 6.1 *Discharge treatment techniques and pollutants*

	Oil separator	Ponds	Swales	Infiltration basins	Filter drains and strips	Sediment tanks	Dynamic separators	Biofilter
BOD [a]		•	•	•		•	•	•
COD [b]	•	•	•	•		•	•	•
Concrete, cement		•	•	•	•	•	•	•
Metals, metalloids		•			•			
Oils and hydrocarbons	•	•	•	•	•		•	
Organic toxic matter (including pesticides)		•				•		
pH		•				•		
Silt and suspended solids		•	•	•	•	•	•	•
Ammonia and nitrogen (TKN)		•	•	•	•			•

[a] BOD, biochemical oxygen demand

[b] COD, chemical oxygen demand

6.3.2   General techniques

Waste – storage and disposal

Pollution minimisation methods should apply to waste generation and storage on site. Bins or skips should be used for the disposal of items such as fuel oil filters and waste oil from vehicle maintenance. The bins or skips should be clearly identified as being separate from general putrescible types of site waste. Waste minimisation via careful planning will help to reduce the potential for pollution incidents.

Sewage discharges to foul sewer, septic tanks or cesspools

A significant proportion of water pollution occurs because waste disposal is incorrectly connected to the drainage leaving a site. Simple mistakes of this nature can be eliminated by careful planning and approach to the positioning of site discharges.

6.3.3   Techniques for the control of surface water

On the majority of sites, discharge of water is inevitable throughout the construction process. The commonest pollutants likely to enter a receiving waterbody are suspended solids, oils (hydrocarbons) and concrete by-products. Ensuring that any wastewater passes through an appropriate treatment process is integral to best management practice. The methods put in place should be appropriate to the level of risk and the sensitivity of the adjacent environment. A combination of treatment methods can be used to provide the required level of pollutant removal dependent on site constraints.

This section discusses the various types of treatment techniques available and their effect on the control of pollutants discharged from construction sites.

Oil separators

Oil separators or petrol interceptors remove floating pollutants, including most hydrocarbons, from site runoff water. These devices have been used for many years in the permanent works for car parks, highways, oil filling areas etc. However, their use for temporary works has been less common.

There are two types of separators: bypass and full retention. Bypass separators are designed for the control of spillages and have the capacity to treat flows generated by the majority of storms (typical rainfall intensity of up to 5 mm/h). Flows greater than this are bypassed by the separator (Figure 6.36). Full retention separators are specified to treat the peak design flow for a particular system and so are both more efficient and more costly than bypass separators.

Most separators are constructed from prefabricated glass reinforced plastic (GRP) structures divided into several individual chambers, which are installed below ground and surrounded by concrete for stability. The size of the interceptor is usually determined by reference to the manufacturer's tables, which give a maximum drained area and percentage impermeability for a particular separator. Water passes through each chamber and is retained for sufficient time to allow any immiscible (floating) pollutants to accumulate on the surface. The flow from one chamber to the next is restricted by a weir, which retains the immiscible pollutants. The separator needs periodic maintenance in normal conditions and must be emptied immediately after a spillage incident.

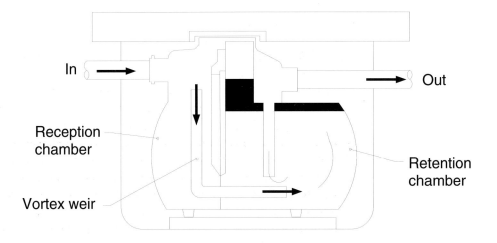

In → ... → Out

Reception chamber

Retention chamber

Vortex weir

Figure 6.36   *Schematic diagram of a bypass oil separator*

Increasingly, separators are being replaced by sustainable urban drainage systems and developers may wish to discuss this option with the appropriate environment regulator. See *Sustainable urban drainage systems – design manual for Scotland and Northern Ireland* (CIRIA C521, 2000) and *Sustainable urban drainage systems – design manual for England and Wales* (CIRIA C522, 2000).

The prevention of oil pollution from construction sites may well involve the use of a below-ground oil/water separator. The production of a European standard design for prefabricated oil separators will empower the UK agencies to require all newly installed oil separators to comply with the Draft European Standard prEN 858: *Installations for separation of light liquids (eg oil and petrol)*.

This standard refers to two "classes" of separator. Class 1 separators are designed to achieve a concentration of less than 5 mg/l of oil under test conditions and are proposed for use where small droplets of oil have to be removed from surface water. Most class 1 units have shut-off valves and oil detection monitors; most are permanently installed.

Class 2 separators are designed to achieve a concentration of less than 100 mg/l of oil under test conditions. They are proposed for use where a lower standard is required, such as trapping spillage or where discharge from a separator passes to foul sewer.

Both types of separator can be installed to operate as "full retention" or "bypass" units. Full retention systems are designed to have the capacity to treat the full flow of a particular site drainage system. This is accepted as being based on a calculated flow equivalent to a rainfall intensity of 50 mm/h. Bypass systems are designed to treat all flows generated by rainfall rates of up to 5 mm/h, which is accepted as covering 99 per cent of all rainfall events. Any flows greater than 5 mm/h bypass the separator unit. These separators are designed to trap oil spillage.

Ponds

The use of ponds to store site runoff water is one of the most effective treatment methods available. (Figure 6.26 illustrates both poor and effective use of ponds.) They are particularly useful for larger construction sites where the attenuation of storm flows and flood prevention are also required and where bulk earthworks form a significant part of the project (see Case study 31). A pond provides a highly effective method of containing any discharged water for quality monitoring or any other required treatment. The BOD and COD of the impounded water can be regulated together with normalisation of pH and retention of suspended solids. Typical levels of pollutant removal for a 12–15-hour retention time are 60 per cent of suspended solids, 40 per cent of BOD and 10–20 per cent of other pollutants, including nitrates. The design of ponds should take into account the necessary health and safety provisions such as perimeter fencing, access for emergency vehicles and flotation equipment.

There are two forms of pond. A dry pond only fills with water following a storm event, whereas a wet pond contains a permanently impounded volume of water. A wet pond has the advantage of greater capacity for the collection of sediments and removal of organic matter and metals. Nonetheless, it needs careful management in the long term to prevent algal blooms and excessive vegetation growth. Barley straw bales placed in the pond helps control algae, while frequent dredging of the pond during the summer months may prevent excessive build-up of vegetation. *Design of flood storage reservoirs* (CIRIA B14, 1993) provides detailed guidance on sizing ponds and determining the required retention times for settling pollutants.

In the case of suspended solids, settlement ponds offer a simple and effective way of controlling the concentration of substances in discharged water (Figure 6.37). Site runoff or water pumped from excavations is channelled into a pond constructed specifically to allow any suspended solids to settle out before discharge.

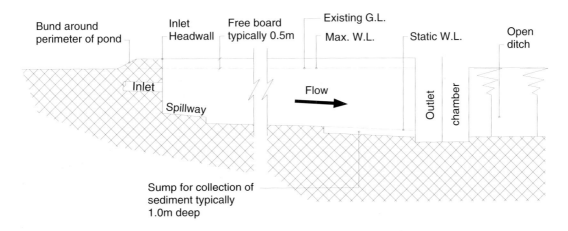

Figure 6.37   *Typical settlement pond cross-section*

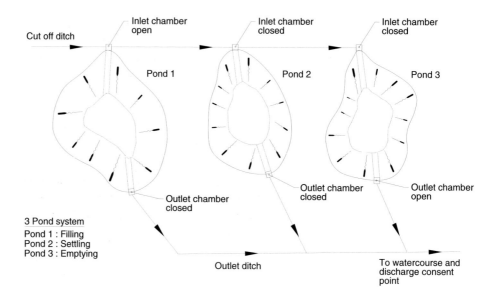

Figure 6.38   *Schematic diagram of a pond system*

Due to the time required for suspended solids to settle, several ponds may be needed. A typical example of a multi-pond arrangement is based on one pond filling, one pond settling out and a third pond emptying (Figure 6.38).

Case study 31 ☺   *Creation of storage ponds*

A major technology centre was to be located adjacent to a wetland site of special scientific interest (SSSI). Consequently, control of pollution from the construction work was a major consideration in the planning and construction stages. The site covers approximately 40 ha. The main activities were diversion of watercourses, bulk earthworks and construction of a number of industrial buildings.

The first programmed operation was the diversion of a reen (an ancient man-made drainage and flood storage channel) from the centre of the site. The construction site had to be segregated from the existing watercourse to prevent pollution. For ecological, landscape and conservation reasons, the diversion had to be completed before the main construction work began.

Due to the fast-track nature of the project, a phased topsoil strip was not possible. To facilitate site drainage and to contain runoff, a series of cutoff ditches were constructed on site. The ditches were interconnected and the flow regulated by weirs. The ditches discharged to a series of settlement ponds that were constructed adjacent to the main works area. In total, three ponds were required due to the topography of the area and to provide sufficient storm runoff storage. The ponds discharged to an adjacent watercourse, with flows regulated by penstocks in the outlet chambers.

Before construction works began on site, a design and method statement for the watercourse diversion and temporary drainage works was prepared and agreed with the Environment Agency and the Internal Drainage Board (IDB). The contractor applied to the EA for a discharge consent, and the temporary drainage scheme was included in the submission. Due to the time required to gain the consent, the application was programmed some way in advance of the works start date.

Flocculating agents may be appropriate in certain circumstances to increase the rate of settlement of suspended solids. However, approval from the relevant environment regulator would be required before their use. Additional purification can be provided by incorporating perforated pipes, geotextiles, straw bales and gravel beds into the pond outlets. Wet ponds can also benefit from the inclusion of biofiltration measures.

If there is a need to provide attenuation of stormwater for the finished development it may be possible to utilise the settlement ponds in the design for the permanent works. The incorporation of dip pipes into settlement pond outlets can prevent oils from being released into the receiving watercourse. Oil booms can also be used on ponds for the same reason. Concreting works can adversely affect pH levels and a settlement pond can contain polluted water for treatment before discharge. A typical design for a pond outlet chamber is given in Figure 6.39.

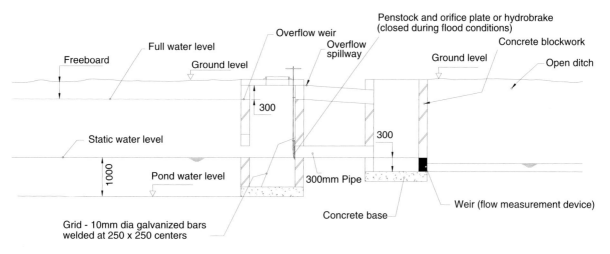

Figure 6.39   *Typical detail of an outlet chamber*

Retention time

The theoretical retention time (t_R) necessary can be determined by several methods, including the Hazen theory or Camp and Vetter formulae (Hazen, 1904; Camp, 1946; Vetter, 1940). These methods determine the conditions needed to achieve the settlement velocity (V_s). The settling velocity varies from 30 mm/s for coarse sand to 0.001 mm/s for fine clay. Based on Hazen's theory, for a given depth of flow d_1, the trap efficiency n, is given by the expression:

$n = V_s \cdot t_R/d_1$

Therefore, rearranging the expression gives the retention time t_R,

$t_R = n \cdot d_1/V_s$

This expression does not consider the effects of flow turbulence, and in practice the actual retention time can be determined by on site inspection.

To provide the required retention time, the pond outflow will need to be throttled to the required level. This can be achieved by the incorporation of fixed or mechanical controls. Fixed controls include orifice plates, pipes weirs, notches or vortex-type controls. Mechanical controls consist of vertical or radial sluice gates, which are usually manually operated but could be electrically operated. Sluice gates also enable the pond system to be isolated in the event of a pollution incident. Further details on determining the required detention time may be found in *Design of flood storage reservoirs* (CIRIA B14, 1993).

Storage volume

The required storage volume is dependent on the retention time and the design rainfall for a particular site. Statistical data for rainfall intensity, duration and frequency for a particular location and return period can be obtained from the Institute of Hydrology Flood Studies Report and the Meteorological Office. Transport and Road Research Laboratory report LR595 (TRRL, 1973) provides guidance on determining the average rainfall intensity for a particular return period.

There are several methods of determining the volume of runoff. However, the basic volume of runoff (V) to the treatment system for a given return period is given by:

$V = Q \cdot D \ (m^3)$

where

inflow rate, $Q = i \cdot Ad \cdot Pr \ (m^3/hour)$

Definitions:

i = rainfall intensity (m/h)
D – rainfall duration (h)
Ad = drained area (m^2)
Pr = permeability allowance.

For temporary works, a return period of one in five years would be appropriate in most circumstances. However, specific design criteria would have to be agreed with the relevant environment protection authority. More detailed information on designing drainage systems can be found in *Sustainable urban drainage systems – design manual for Scotland and Northern Ireland* (CIRIA C521, 2000) and *Sustainable urban drainage systems – design manual for England and Wales* (CIRIA C522, 2000).

6.3.4   Sustainable drainage systems

General background information on sustainable urban drainage systems (SUDS) can be found in the joint Environment Agency and SEPA (1997) publication, *A guide to sustainable urban drainage. Review of the design and management of constructed wetlands* (CIRIA R180, 1998) provides detailed information on biofiltration techniques.

Swales

Swales are open grassed or vegetated channels that fall at a shallow gradient and operate in a similar way to filter strips. Intercepted runoff is directed along such features and the grass or vegetation present retards the water flow and filters out pollutants. To prevent erosion, longitudinal gradients no greater than 6 per cent and water velocities below 0.5 m/s are necessary. Typical performance for a swale 30–60 m long is the filtration of 70 per cent suspended solids and 30–40 per cent of metals, bacteria and hydrocarbons from runoff water.

Together with infiltration basins and filter strips, swales depend on the infiltration and permeability of the surrounding ground and water table level. The level of vegetation also contributes to filtration efficiency. The treatment performance of swales can be increased by construction of weirs or dams across the longitudinal profile to reduce the velocities of water flowing. Swales can be combined to form a network system and used as a means of interconnecting site drainage to settlement ponds.

For the effective use of swales, the vegetation has to be well established before use. Hence, to use swales on a construction site, there has to be sufficient time in the overall site programme for their development.

On small construction projects swales would normally only be used where they were being retained as a permanent surface water treatment system (for example a small roads project).

On large construction sites, swales may be used as a final treatment system for runoff from the built structure, but are unlikely to be capable of use on their own for dealing with construction site drainage. Not withstanding the foregoing, swales can be used as a secondary treatment option for construction runoff after a pond or lagoon. Alternatively, the site of the swale may be used as a settlement pond during construction and modified on completion of building to the swale proper.

Swale design – worked example

The design of a swale has been described in detail in *Sustainable urban drainage systems – design manual for Scotland and Northern Ireland* (CIRIA C521, 2000) and *Sustainable urban drainage systems – design manual for England and Wales* (CIRIA C522, 2000). A worked example from these books is given below, which should be modified for the construction site in question. Particular account should be taken of the permeability of the specific site – ie the percentage of the site that is hard surface. If the swale is to remain as a permanent feature, then the permeability of the completed site should be taken into account. Runoff from a completed site with a large proportion of hard surfaces may be significantly greater than during the construction period.

Example design calculations

1. Estimation of runoff – the runoff can be estimated using the Modified Rational Method (Wallingford, 1981), the Unit Hydrograph Method (Institute of Hydrology, 1985) or the Simplified Flood Estimation Method (*Design of flood storage reservoirs*, CIRIA B14, 1993). A typical calculation based on a "block" hyetograph is as follows:

$$Q_{max} = (1/360) \cdot p \cdot i \cdot A_p \cdot D \ (m^3/s)$$

where

p = permeability factor (= 1 for 100 per cent impermeable area, typically in the range 0.4–0.75 for a stripped construction site area)

i = rainfall intensity (mm/h) for the design return period

A_p = site area (ha)

D = rainstorm duration (h); the average rainfall intensity is obtained by dividing the rainfall depth by the duration.

2. Design of filter strip – from Manning's equation:

$$Q = \{a \cdot R^{2/3} \cdot s^{1/2}\}/n$$

where:

a = cross sectional area of flow (m^2)
R = hydraulic radius (= a/wetted perimeter)
s = ground slope in the direction of flow (m/m)
n = Manning's roughness coefficient.

The value of Manning's n varies depending on the flow parameter and length of grass as shown in Figure 6.40.

For effective treatment to occur the main design criteria are:

depth of flow <0.1 m
velocity <0.3 m/s
longitudinal gradient <0.05 (1 in 20).

For a particular filter strip width, ground slope and grass length, Manning's equation is solved by iteration based on an initial assumption for n to provide a value for the depth of flow. The variables are then adjusted as necessary to meet the required design criteria.

3. Design of a swale – for a swale that is designed for treatment by filtration, the procedure for design shown above for filter strips can be used. Swales can also be designed to operate by infiltration and further design guidance is given in BRE (1991) and *Infiltration drainage – manual of good practice* (CIRIA R156, 1996).

Using BRE 365:

inflow – outflow = storage
outflow = $1/F$ a_{S50} H soil infiltration rate H storm duration

where:

a_{S50} = surface area of swale sides to 50 per cent of effective depth
F = safety factor.

4. Typical calculations

(a) Filter strip design

Site area, $A_p = 0.25$ ha

For assumed times of entry of 5 min and five-year return period:

rainfall intensity, $i = 88.5$ mm/h
assumed permeability factor $= 0.5$
$Q_{max} = 1/360 \times 0.5 \times 88.5 \times 0.25 = 0.03$ m³/s.

For a filter strip with grass length 50–150 mm, 1 m wide with longitudinal slope of 0.02:

assume depth of flow $= 0.100$ m
assume $n = 0.1$

From Manning's equation:

$Q = 1/n\,[\,a \cdot R^{2/3} \cdot S^{1/2}\,]$
$Q_{capacity} = 1/0.1\,[\,0.1 \times (0.1/1.2)^{2/3} \times 0.02^{1/2}\,] = 0.027$ m³/s

Check velocity:

$Q = V \cdot A$
$V = 0.027/0.1 = 0.27$ m/s < 0.3

Check assumption for n:

$V \cdot R = 0.27 \times 0.1/1.2 = 0.023$

from graph (Figure 6.40), $n = 0.098$, implying that the assumption is satisfactory.

(b) Infiltration drainage design

Inflow – outflow = storage
Outflow $= 1/F\,(a_{S50} \times$ soil infiltration rate $\times$ storm duration)

For an assumed maximum flooded depth of 0.5m:

$a_{S50} = 0.5\,(2 \times 0.5) + 1.0 = 1.5$ m

Take infiltration rate $= 0.008$ m/h

For a 4 h (240 min) storm duration period, and factor of safety $= 5$:

outflow $= 1/5\,(\,1.5 \times 0.008 \times 240) = 0.576$ m²/m

For an infiltration trench 100 m long:

outflow $= 0.576 \times 100 = 57.6$ m³

From CIRIA Report 156: $M_{10\text{-}4} = 9.33$ mm/h (for $r = 0.33$):

$M_{10\text{-}4} =$ 10-year intensity for 4 h duration

For a site area of 0.3 ha (3000 m²):

inflow $= 3000 \times 9.33 \times 10^{-3} \times 4 = 112$ m³
storage $= 112 - 57.6 = 54$ m²

Check depth of flooding:

depth $= 54/100(1) = 0.540$, so assumed flooded depth of 0.5 m is satisfactory.

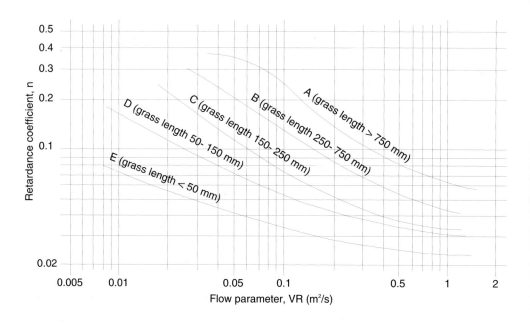

Figure 6.40 *Manning's n for different grass lengths (CIRIA, 1990)*

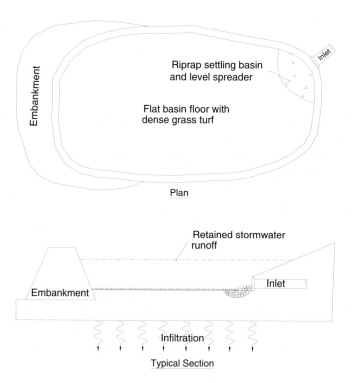

Figure 6.41 *Infiltration basin*

Infiltration basins

Infiltration basins are designed to provide water storage using a surface reservoir that will allow infiltration of the impounded volume of water through the base into the underlying ground (Figure 6.41). In common with swales, filter drains and filter strips, the performance of these structures depends mainly on the infiltration and permeability of the surrounding ground and the depth to the groundwater table. Infiltration basins can serve catchment areas of up to 10 ha depending upon the local conditions. Detailed design guidance is contained in *Infiltration drainage – manual of good practice* (CIRIA R156, 1996).

The size of an infiltration basin depends on the inflow from the construction site and the ground permeability. Section 6.3.3 discusses the method for determining the volume of runoff. The permeability can be determined using the test procedure set out in BRE (1991), which involves determining the time taken for a specific quantity of water to percolate from an excavation to calculate the permeability coefficient.

Filter strips

Filter strips are existing vegetated areas of land that are used to accept surface water runoff from an upstream area. The selection of suitable areas is subject to agreement with the relevant regulator, but they can provide an effective method of treatment for smaller sites of up to 2 ha.

Filter strips carry runoff as overland sheet flow, removing suspended solids and discharging to the groundwater system by infiltration. The efficiency of a filter strip depends on the type of vegetation present with narrow grassed strips, typically removing up to 25 per cent of suspended solids and wider wooded strips removing up to 80 per cent suspended solids. Filter strips are unlikely to be adequate as a sole treatment method for site runoff. They are normally used in conjunction with other methods.

Filter strips are not suitable for a high suspended particle load as they can easily become smothered, requiring time for vegetation regrowth. They should only be used in locations that will produce small amounts of silt, therefore.

Filter beds and drains

Filter beds and drains consist of areas of granular material together with geotextiles and other filter media through which water is passed to remove pollutants (Figures 6.42 and 6.43). Filter drains act as a form of linear infiltration feature and are best suited to situations where groundwater pollution is not a major issue. They can be adopted as a primary treatment method or used in conjunction with other treatment methods for secondary treatment before discharge. For example, the inflow could be pre-treated using a settlement tank, or the filter drain could be connected to the inlet of a settlement pond. For smaller sites where the creation of ponds is not practical, filter drains and beds fulfil a similar function in the removal of pollutants, including suspended solids.

Important considerations in the use of filter drains are the infiltration rate and the permeability of the surrounding ground, the normal depth to the water table, and the response of existing groundwater to precipitation. Infiltration rates of the surrounding ground usually need to be greater than 12.5 mm/h for a filter drain to be effective.

The pollution control performance of filter drains is typically 90 per cent suspended solids removal, and 60 per cent phosphorus and 90 per cent coliform removal from supply waters. Filter beds can be used to normalise the pH level of runoff before discharge, with limestone chippings, for example, being used to treat acidic (low pH) water.

Sedimentation tanks

Sedimentation tanks are purpose-made structures to contain water for the removal of suspended solids. They operate on similar principles to detention ponds and are an effective method of isolating the existing groundwater system from the site drainage. The size of the tank is determined by the permissible rate of discharge and the drained area. Assessment of the storage volume required can be calculated in the same way as for settlement ponds, and several individual tanks can be used if required.

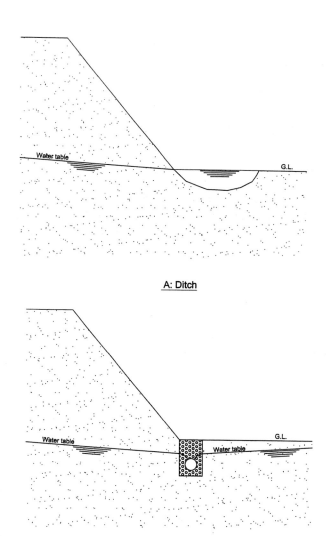

A: Ditch

B: French drain

Figure 6.42   *Schematic section showing water control methods*

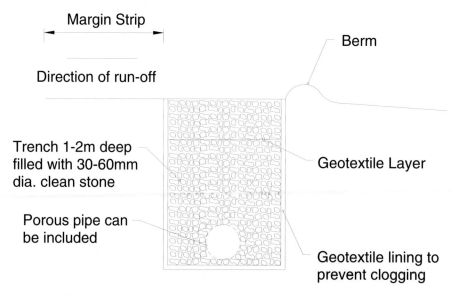

Margin Strip

Direction of run-off

Berm

Trench 1-2m deep
filled with 30-60mm
dia. clean stone

Geotextile Layer

Porous pipe can
be included

Geotextile lining to
prevent clogging

Figure 6.43   *Typical filter drain detail*

Dynamic separator

Dynamic separators are purpose-made devices that separate several pollutants from site water (Figure 6.44). For smaller construction sites, where there is insufficient space for the construction of settlement ponds or tanks, the use of dynamic separators can be effective in retaining solids and oils. The manufacturers of these devices produce a specific design based on the peak flows, sediment grading and removal efficiency.

Dynamic separators typically retain particles as small as 75 microns with an overall removal efficiency of around 90 per cent of particles greater than 150 microns. In some cases it may be possible to include a permanent drainage scheme requiring a dynamic separator in the temporary works to reduce costs.

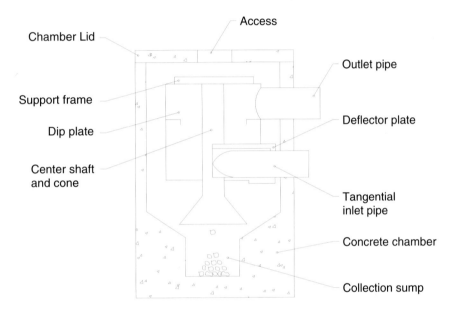

Figure 6.44   *Schematic diagram of a dynamic separator*

Biofiltration techniques

The biofiltration treatment method is based on the interaction of vegetation and soil with site runoff (Figure 6.45 and CIRIA Report 180, 1998). The method is incorporated in filter strips and swales together with some wet ponds. It uses either naturally occurring or introduced vegetation. Biofiltration is not suitable for the treatment of non-biodegradable pollutants and its effectiveness varies according to the time of year. The use of this system requires careful consideration, therefore.

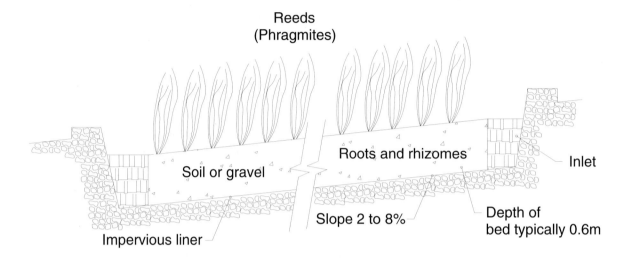

Reeds
(Phragmites)

Roots and rhizomes

Inlet

Soil or gravel

Slope 2 to 8%

Depth of
bed typically 0.6m

Impervious liner

Figure 6.45   *Typical detail of a biofiltration system*

6.4   INCIDENT CONTROL AND EMERGENCY PROCEDURES

The provision and adaptation of a contingency plan for pollution emergencies either within or separate to the site operation plan should be an essential element of any construction project. Such a plan should be developed during the project design and implementation stages so that it becomes an integral part of the site operational procedures from the outset of the project (see Case study 32).

The contingency plan should identify the actions to be taken in the event of pollution incident. It should include details of emergency contacts and professional pollution clean-up companies located near a development (Site procedures 10 and 11 – Figures 6.46 and 6.47). A PPG note will be available on contingency planning in 2000.

It is important that, in an emergency, site personnel do not have to spend valuable time establishing what should be done via line management. Rather, personnel should be able to take immediate temporary measures to forestall the entry of pollutants to controlled waters. Contingency planning procedures must be regularly reviewed to include changes to site operations that were not foreseen during design. Figure 6.27 illustrates the damage caused by oil spills and some good practice regarding emergency procedures.

Even when all reasonably practicable measures have been taken, pollution incidents that have the potential to significantly affect water quality in the vicinity of the site may still occur during the construction phase of a project. For a potential incident, the main criteria are prevention, containment and treatment. Section 6.2 deals with the prevention of incidents and containment of relevant activities, while treatment methods are discussed in Section 6.3. The preparation of contingency plans that contain emergency response procedures to be followed in the event of a pollution incident is an important part of the management of a construction site.

The procedures need to be prepared in conjunction with the assessment of the risk of a pollution incident occurring and the measures to be taken to minimise pollution. The location of the procedures should be publicised and it is essential that they are set out clearly so that they can easily be understood and acted upon.

The emergency procedures can include the following:

- containment measures
- emergency discharge routes
- list of appropriate equipment and clean-up materials
- maintenance schedule for equipment
- details of trained staff, location, and provision for 24-hour cover
- details of staff responsibilities
- notification procedures to inform the relevant environment protection authority
- audit and review schedule
- telephone numbers of statutory water undertakers and local water company
- list of specialist pollution clean-up companies and their telephone numbers.

The emergency procedure needs to be reviewed regularly to ensure any developments in working on site are taken into account. Auditing of the pollution prevention plan is also necessary and should include monitoring of discharged water quality to ensure compliance with the set discharge limits. A schedule of audits is necessary and should be organised to take account of the construction programme.

On some projects there may be a requirement for an environment liaison officer (ELO) to form part of the site supervision team. The staff responsible for the co-ordination of a response to a pollution incident, who are identified in the emergency procedure written for a particular project, need to liaise with the appointed ELO on a day-to-day basis. Some of the equipment and methods that can be used in the control of a pollution incident and the types of pollutant affected are shown in Table 6.2.

Table 6.2 *Pollution control equipment and methods*

Equipment and methods	Pollutant affected
Close outlet gate valve	All by containment
Sand bags	All by containment
Bunding	All by containment
Sand	Oils and concrete etc
Oil booms	Oils and floatables
Pollution blankets	Oils and floatables
Oil soak-up material	Oils and floatables
Straw bales	Suspended solids and oils

Where there is existing sewerage for domestic or trade wastes it may be possible to discharge directly to a wastewater system in an emergency. This may provide an effective contingency measure for dealing with a pollution incident on site but would be subject to the agreement and requirements of the relevant water company or operator of the wastewater system. The removal of polluted water off site by tanker may need to be considered in certain circumstances, depending on the type and level of pollution. The removal of polluted materials from the site would be subject to the duty of care and would need to be discussed with the appropriate environment regulator.

Case study 32 ☺   Development of site emergency procedures

A major road scheme crossing numerous environmentally sensitive rivers and water-course, had a large workforce and many subcontractors, so well-defined emergency procedures were of paramount importance. The procedures were drawn up in case of oil/pollutant spillage, water pollution, or dust pollution. They were agreed with all relevant parties including the Environment Agency. They were simple and clear, with all parties named in the procedure knowing their role.

At the most vulnerable locations signs were posted to ensure people at the location remembered the procedure. The procedures and notices were kept up to date and the situations monitored. Emergency procedures included:

- call-out numbers for assistance (radio, phone in and out of hours)

- Environment Agency call-out

- spill kits and spare booms carried in all refuelling vehicles; stock held in the stores.

Bildem Civil Engineering Ltd

New Road

Site Procedure 10 – Control of pollution incidents

Revision 0, issued 01/01/2000

In the event of the pollution of any watercourse, contact:

Bildem Base

By radio   **Call sign – Bildem Base**

By phone   **01222 XXXXXX**

Out of hours   **01222 XXXXXX** (security gate)

Bildem Base will follow Site Procedure 11 *Control of pollution incidents – action by stores base*, issued in conjunction with this notice, to notify appropriate personnel.

Out of hours, Catchem Security will alert the duty foremen.

This procedure is to be displayed in all site offices, adjacent to phone points where applicable, at bridges and adjacent to watercourses, and added to your Procedure Folder.

For Bildem Civil Engineering Ltd

[*signed by person responsible*]

I K Brunel
Project Manager

Circulation: all site staff.

Figure 6.46   *Site procedure 10 – control of pollution incidents*

Bildem Civil Engineering Ltd

New Road

Site Procedure 11
Control of pollution incidents – action by Stores Base

Revision 0, issued 01/01/2000

Further to Site Procedure 10 issued in conjunction with this notice, and also Site Procedures 1, 5 and 6, stores staff are to note the actions below in the event of a pollution incident being notified from site.

Following an alert from site, Base must notify the following of the location and type of incident:

FIRST   WORKS SUPERINTENDENT John Smith

Call sign   John

Mobile phone   0836 XXXXXX

SECOND   AREA A: GENERAL FOREMAN Joe Bloggs

Call sign   Joe

Mobile phone   0836 XXXXXX

AREA B: GENERAL FOREMAN Dave Evans

Call sign   Dave

Mobile phone   0836 XXXXXX

THIRD   In all cases, ensure that Big Roads Engineering Consultancy is aware of the incident.

The works superintendent or deputy must report all incidents to the Environment Agency.

Figure 6.47   *Site procedure 11 – control of pollution incidents, action by stores base*

7 Summary and recommendations

This guidance provides practical help for consultants and contractors on how to plan and manage construction projects to prevent, or at least minimise, water pollution. It addresses water quality issues from inception of a construction project, completion of the construction stage, and into demolition and site clearance. It describes the sources and movement of water through a construction site, along with the types of water pollution often associated with site activities. The book also defines the chemical properties of natural waterbodies and commonly encountered indicators of water pollution. It details the legislative framework controlling water quality as well as the associated health and safety issues and the schemes used by regulators to categorise the severity of pollution incidents.

The guidance is generally relevant for all types of contract conditions – traditional, design-and-build, design-build-finance-operate (DBFO) and partnering. With some types of contract the contractor carries the risk of cost or programme delays caused by unexpected events or occurrences relating to water quality issues. It is the responsibility of the contractor to be aware of the relevant issues and to manage the site effectively so that damage does not occur to the water environment. If in doubt, guidance should be sought from the company's environmental representative, an environmental consultant or environmental regulator.

Environmental concerns may arise at any stage in the construction process and the number of water pollution incidents that occur because of site works highlights the need for improved environmental performance within the industry. People working in construction ought to be aware of their environmental obligations and the benefits that good practice will bring at every stage from the initial feasibility studies through to design, construction planning and the actual works on site. Just as the environmental issues differ at each stage, the approaches to resolving them may also differ accordingly. The consequences of environmental planning, or lack of planning, by people involved in the early stages of a project's development can profoundly affect the ability of site staff to meet their obligations. Because of this, other construction professionals should seek to understand the site environmental good practice presented in this guidance document.

Some of the advice offered here is based on the good practices that have been carried out on construction sites for many years, but many of the ideas are contemporary. There is other ongoing research into the control of water pollution, and users of this document should be aware that good practice will develop in parallel with this. This guidance document is designed to inform all levels of construction staff, from the young site engineer to the experienced site manager. The successful control of water pollution on construction sites relies on a planned and integrated approach. This book, therefore, is relevant to all organisations represented on a construction site, whether as a client, promoter, designer, main contractor or a subcontractor.

The detailed research undertaken in "Control of water pollution – guidance for consultants and contractors" (CIRIA RP585) was carried out by Hyder Consulting and COSTAIN Civil Engineering. In addition to the good practice provided in this report, the study has also identified a series of recommendations for additional developments to assist the construction industry in improving its environmental performance.

These recommendations are set out below and were developed by CIRIA's research contractor in consultation with CIRIA, the project steering group and construction industry delegates to the four focus group meetings that took place during the research project (see Acknowledgements).

Small to medium enterprise (SME) guide and site training pack

A major issue highlighted during this study is that it is extremely difficult to disseminate good practice information to all involved in the construction process. It is essential that good practice is provided at the right levels of detail, and in the correct formats, if all those involved in construction are to understand and use the information effectively. The information required by a consultant designer, for example, differs from that needed by a main civil engineering contractor, as does that required by building contractors. The information used on site will not be the same as that used in the design office and the data essential for a small, short-term project will vary from that on a multimillion-pound long-term project.

This report has bought together a wide range of information relevant to the prevention of water pollution and has developed a wide range of good practice procedures. In its current format the guidance is most likely to be used in the planning and development stage of a project before work starts on site. However, there is a clear need to provide guidance and training for construction staff working on site on a daily basis. This guidance material should ideally be supported by a training pack that site managers can use as part of site induction courses for all site staff. This information should be prepared noting the useful Environment Agency pack "Building a Cleaner Future" and CIRIA's recently published training pack Environmental Good Practice on site.

> *Recommendation:*   ***Preparation of a simplified guide for SMEs and on-site staff, and a site training pack.***

A voluntary code of practice

Knowing the acceptable methods and procedures for the control of water pollution on site is not always easy. This is especially true for contractors that have not worked closely with the environment regulator when developing a project. While most contractors are aware of the environment regulator's prosecution powers, they are not always aware of their advisory services and there is a reluctance to seek advice. The environment regulator's Pollution Prevention Guidance notes (PPGs)* do provide some very useful guidance. However, a voluntary code of practice that builds on the PPGs and this project would provide a valuable insight for contractors into the environment regulator's expectations for works on construction sites. The development of a voluntary code of practice would facilitate the use of environmental good practice as a standard rather than an exception. It would also allow clients to specify minimum environmental standards in selecting a construction contractor and assist them in assessing contractors' on-site performance.

* Note: The DETR also produces Planning Policy Guidance (PPGs); these should not be confused.

> *Recommendation:*   ***The preparation of a voluntary code of practice for the control of water pollution on construction sites that builds on the environment regulator's PPGs and the good practice presented in this guidance to provide a benchmark of procedures approved by the environment regulator.***

Further information on pollution incidents

The Environment Agency's pollution incident figures for England and Wales (see Section 2.6) have shown that the numbers of pollution incidents from construction sites have continued to increase in recent years. The information also indicates that there have been changes in the character of incidents resulting from construction. Many recent incidents have been quite small and relate to suspended solids and oil. However, these data do not allow us to identify the parts of the industry and types of construction activity that are causing the pollution incidents.

Different parts of the construction industry require different types of guidance and advice. For guidance to be more accurately targeted, and hence become more effective, more needs to be known about the sectors of the industry that are committing offences, the nature of pollution being caused and the type of projects causing it. Is it, for example, large contractors on long-term projects, short-term maintenance contracts, or small housebuilders with a short construction period?

Recommendation: *Refinement of the Environment Agency, SEPA and DoE (NI) pollution incident databases to allow identification of size of construction company, the type/size/duration of project and the nature of the pollution incident. A database format common to all regulators would further facilitate use of the information.*

Guidance through the development control system

Before most development begins in the UK, some form of consent is required from the competent authorities. Disseminating guidance at the planning stage, for example by sending out information with planning forms, would help cut the number of pollution incidents. Alternatively, when giving a project permission to proceed, the competent authority, where appropriate, should consider adding conditions to the consents that control the works on the construction site and prevent damage to the environment.

The competent authority could issue a standard information pack or leaflet to the developer or his/her agent with the development consent. This pack would highlight the potential environmental impacts and risks associated with construction operations, and would direct the reader to sources of guidance.

Action during the initial development consent period provides an opportunity to highlight the issues, both to consultants and to the clients promoting the development. An information pack issued at this stage should advise on the responsibilities of all parties and explain that partnership with the contractor is the key to success.

Recommendation: *The competent authority should consider adding conditions to control works on construction sites when giving consent for works to proceed.*

Recommendation: *Provision of a pack or leaflet for issue by the competent authority when a consent is sent to the applicant.*

Environmental performance indicators for contractors

Current schemes for environmental accreditation (both national certification schemes such as ISO 14001, and industry-led awards such as the Considerate Contractor scheme) should be reviewed to identify the potential for creating a system of environmental performance indicators for contractors. Clients and consultants should consider a contractor's environmental credentials when procuring and selecting them for work.

Recommendation: *Development of environmental performance indicators for contractors and their use in procurement and selection of contractors.*

Clear identification of the costs of causing pollution

The penalties that may result from prosecution for causing water pollution can be severe, particularly if the hidden costs accruing to the polluter are taken into account. In addition to legal fees, for example, the polluter may have to pay clean-up costs and extra staff costs to cover the time spend defending a case. To these must be added the value of lost contracts through loss of reputation. Contractors with a poor environmental performance often overlook these costs. Such companies may compare the likelihood of getting caught and prosecuted (and the direct cost of being prosecuted) with the cost of educating staff and adopting appropriate procedures for the control of water pollution on site. Clearly identifying the expense to a company of causing pollution will help to change attitudes to that cost and will provide a direct incentive to adopt good practice. It would also encourage adoption of good practice to highlight the minimal additional cost that the well-planned application of good pollution prevention techniques may mean.

Recommendation: *Develop techniques for the clear identification of the costs of water pollution, highlighting the true cost of pollution incidents from construction using case studies.*

8 References

Alabaster, J S, Calamari, D, Dethlefsen V, Konemann, H, Lloyd, R and Solbé, J F, 1987, *Water quality criteria for European freshwater fish*. EIRAC Technical Paper 37

BRE, 1991, *Soakaway design*. Building Research Establishment Digest 365
(NB this replaces BRE Digest 151 *Percolation testing*)

British Standard Institution, 1982, BS 5911 *Concrete pipes and ancillary concrete products*

Camp, T R, 1946, *Sedimentation and the design of settling tanks*. Transactions of the American Society of Civil Engineers

Chapman, D (ed), 1996, *Water quality assessments*. Cambridge University Press

CIRIA, 1989, *The engineering implications of rising groundwater levels in the deep aquifer below London*. CIRIA Special Publication 69 (ISBN 0 86017 303 8)

CIRIA, 1990, *Use of vegetation in civil engineering*. CIRIA Book 10
(ISBN 0 408 03849 70)

CIRIA, 1993, *Rising groundwater levels in Birmingham and the engineering implications*. CIRIA Special Publication 92 (ISBN 0 86017 364 X)

CIRIA, 1993, *Design of flood storage reservoirs*. CIRIA Book 14
(ISBN 0 7506 1057 3)

CIRIA, 1996, *Infiltration drainage – manual of good practice*. CIRIA Report 156
(ISBN 0-86017-457-3)

CIRIA, 1997a, *Construction of bunds for oil storage tanks*. CIRIA Report 163
(ISBN 0-86017-468-9)

CIRIA, 1997b, *CDM Regulations – work sector guidance for designers*. CIRIA Report 166 (ISBN 0-86017-464-6)

CIRIA, 1998, *Review of the design and management of constructed wetlands*. CIRIA Report 180 (ISBN 0 86017 485 9)

CIRIA, 1999, *Hydraulic measures for the control and treatment of groundwater pollution*. CIRIA Report 186 (ISBN 0 86017 499 9)

CIRIA, 2000a, *Groundwater control – design and practice*. CIRIA Publication C515
(ISBN 0 86017 515 4)

CIRIA, 2000b, *Sustainable urban drainage systems design manual for Scotland and Northern Ireland* (CIRIA Publication C521, 2000, ISBN 0 86017 521 9)

CIRIA, 2000c, *Sustainable urban drainage systems design manual for England and Wales* (CIRIA Publication C522, 2000, ISBN 0 86017 522 7)

CIRIA and Environment Agency joint guidelines: *Masonry bunds for oil storage tanks* and *Concrete bunds for oil storage tanks*

County Planning Officers (CPOs) Society, 1995, *Planning for quality in minerals and waste development control – a contribution by the County Planning Officers' Society to the ongoing discussion about improvements to the quality of development control*

Draft European Standard prEN 858 *Installations for separation of light liquids (eg oil and petrol)*

Dyer, K R, 1986, *Coastal and estuarine sediment dynamics*. Chichester: Wiley

EH40, 1998, *Occupational exposure limits 1998*. Health and Safety Executive Guidance Note (ISBN 0 7176 1474 3)

Environment Agency guidelines (various):

- *River pollution and how to avoid it*
- *Chemical pollution and how to avoid it*
- *Solvent pollution and how to avoid it*
- *Silt pollution and how to avoid it*
- *Follow the oil care code*
- *Oil care at work*

Environment Agency, 1997, *Assessing water quality – general quality assessment (GQA) scheme for biology*. Fact Sheet, Environment Agency

Environment Agency, 1998a, *Policy and practice for the protection of groundwater*

Environment Agency, 1998b, *River habitat quality – the physical character of rivers and streams in the UK and Isle of Man* (Report no 2, Joint Publication with SEPA and EHS (ISBN 1 873160 42 9)

Environment Agency, 1999, *Water pollution incidents in England and Wales 1998*

Environment Agency, Environment and Heritage, and SEPA pollution prevention guidelines (PPGs):

- PPG1 – *General guide to the prevention of pollution of controlled waters*
- PPG2 – *Above ground oil storage tanks*
- PPG5 – *Works in, near or liable to affect watercourses*
- PPG6 – *Working at demolition and construction sites*
- PPG8 – *Safe storage and disposal of used oils*
- PPG9 – *The prevention of pollution of controlled waters by pesticides*
- PPG (draft) – *Maintenance of structures over water*

Environment Agency and SEPA, 1997, A guide to sustainable urban drainage

Environment and Heritage Service, 1995, *River quality in Northern Ireland*. Belfast: EHS

Hazen, A, 1904, *On sedimentation*. Transactions of the American Society of Civil Engineers

Health and Safety Commission, 1988 3rd edition, *Control of Substances Hazardous to Health Regulations 1988 – Approved codes of practice*. London: HMSO (ISBN 0 11-885698 7 pp 62–57, 90, 114–115)

Health and Safety Commission, 1995a, *Designing for health and safety in construction – a guide for designers on the Construction (Design and Management) Regulations 1994*. HSB Books (ISBN 0 7176 0807 7)

Health and Safety Commission, 1995b, *Managing construction for health and safety. Construction (Design and Management) Regulations 1994. Approved code of practice.* HSE Books

Institution of Chemical Engineers, 1995, *Model form of conditions for process plant – Suitable for lump sum contracts.* Rugby: Institution of Chemical Engineers (ISBN 0 85295 326 7)

Institution of Civil Engineers, 1990, *Pollution and its containment.* London: Thomas Telford

Institute of Hydrology, 1995, *Flood studies report*

ISO 9001, 1994, BS EN ISO 9001 *Quality systems. Model for quality assurance in design, development, production, installation and servicing*

ISO 14001, 1996, *Environmental management systems – Specifications with guidance for use*

Joint Contracts Tribunal, 1980, *Standard form of building contract.* JCT80

Kotz, J C and Purcell, K F, 1987, *Chemistry and chemical reactivity.* Philadelphia, PA: Saunders College

Latham M, 1994, *Constructing the team*, Final report of the government industry review of procurement and contractual arrangements in the UK construction industry (also known as "The Latham Report"). London: HMSO

Luker, M and Montague, K, 1994, *Control of pollution from highway drainage discharge.* CIRIA Report 142 (ISBN 0 86017 415 8)

Ministry of Agriculture Fisheries and Food (MAFF) and Health and Safety Commission (HSC), 1990 2nd edition, *Code of practice for safe use of pesticides on farms and holdings.* Part III of Food and Environmental Protection Act 1985 (FEPA) and the Health and Safety at Work Act 1974 Combined Code. MAFF

Ministry of Agriculture Fisheries (MAFF), 1991, *Code of good agricultural practice for the protection of water*

Manahan, S E, 1990, *Hazardous waste chemistry, toxicology and treatment.* Michigan: Lewis

Manahan, S E, 1994 6th edition, *Environmental chemistry.* London: Lewis

McNeill, A "Road construction and river pollution in South-West Scotland" in *J.CIWEM*, June 1996, pp 175–182

Moss, B, 1992, *Ecology of freshwaters – man and medium.* Oxford: Blackwell Scientific

National Rivers Authority, 1994, *Contaminated land and the water environment.* 1994 Report of the National Rivers Authority

NEC, 1995, 2nd edition, *Engineering and construction sub-contract (ECS).* London: Thomas Telford

OFTEC, 1995, OCP2 *For the safe storage of oil fuel at commercial, agricultural and domestic premises*

SEPA, 1997, *A guide to sustainable urban drainage*

SEPA, 1998, *Water pollution by oil*

SEPA, 1999, *Improving Scotland's water environment* (available from SEPA website)

Taylor, P, Shemmings, S and Francis, S, 1995, *Construction, law and the environment.* Cameron May

Transport and Road Research Laboratory and Young, C P, 1973, *Estimated rainfall for drainage calculations in the United Kingdom.* TRRL *Report LR595*

Vetter, C P, 1040, *Technical aspects of the silt problem on the Colorado river.* Civil Engineering

Wallingford, 1981, *Modified rational method.* Wallingford Procedure

Water Services Association. 1990, *General conditions of contract for water industry plant contractors.* Water Services Association Publications, October 1990, Form G/90.

Directives

European Community Directive *Council Directive on the quality of surface water intended for the abstraction of drinking water* (75/440/EEC)

European Community Directive *Council Directive concerning the quality of bathing water* (76/160/EEC)

European Community Directive *Council Directive on the quality of freshwaters needing protection or improvement in order to support fish life* (78/659/EEC)

European Community Directive *Council Directive on the protection of groundwater against pollution caused by certain dangerous substances* (80/68/EEC)

European Community Directive *Council Directive relating to the quality of water intended for human consumption* (80/77/EEC)

European Community Directive *Council Directive concerning urban waste water treatment* (91/271/EEC)

European Community Directive *Council Directive on the implementation of minimum safety and health requirements at temporary and mobile construction sites* (92/57/EEC)

Legislation

Anti-Pollution Works Regulations 1999, SI no 1006

Confined Spaces Regulations 1997

Construction, Design and Management Regulations 1994, SI no 3140,

Construction (Head Protection) Regulations 1989

Construction (Health and Safety, Welfare) Regulations 1996, SI no 1592

Control of Asbestos at Work Regulations 1987

Control of Major Accident Regulations 1999, SI no 743

Control of Pesticides Regulations 1986, SI no 1510

Control of Pollution Act 1974

Control of Pollution (Special Waste) Regulations 1980, SI no 1709

Control of Substances Hazardous to Health (COSHH) Regulations 1998

Drainage Northern Ireland Order 1973

Environment Act 1995, SI no 1984

Environmental Protection Act 1990

Fisheries Act 1966

Food and Environmental Protection Act (FEPA) 1985, SI no 1516

Groundwater Regulations 1998, SI no 2746

Groundwater Regulations (Northern Ireland) 1998

Health and Safety at Work Act 1974

Management of Health and Safety at Work 1992, SI no 2051

Management of Health and Safety at Work (amendments) 1994, SI no 2865

Management of Health and Safety at Work Regulations 1992

Manual Handling Operations Regulations 1992

Noise at Work Regulations 1989.

Personal Protective Equipment at Work Regulations 1992

Sea Fisheries (Consolidation and Amendment) Regulations (Northern Ireland) 1972

Surface Waters (Dangerous Substances) (Classification) Regulations 1997, SI no 2560

Surface Waters (Dangerous Substances) (Classification) Regulations 1998, SI 1998, no 389

Surface Waters (Dangerous Substances) Regulations (Northern Ireland) 1998, SR no 397.

Surface Waters (Dangerous Substances) (Classification) (Scotland) Regulations 1990

Surface Waters (Dangerous Substances) (Classification) (Scotland) (no 2) Regulations 1998, SI no 1344 (S. 68)

Water Act 1989, SI no 1147

Water and Sewerage Services (Northern Ireland) Order 1973

Water Resources Act 1991

Water Resources Act (Northern Ireland) 1972

9 Further reading

Alabaster, J S and Lloyd, R, 1980, *Water quality criteria for freshwater fish.* Oxford: Butterworths

British Aggregate Construction Materials Industry (BACMI) and Environment Agency, *The use of air cooled blast furnace slag as an unbound aggregate in the construction industry* (joint guideline)

Cave, J D, 1995, "The effects of the Kielder scheme on fisheries" in *Journal of Fish Biology* 27 (Supplement A), pp 109–121

CIRIA, 1994, *Water pollution issues in the construction industry.* Construction Industry Environmental Forum (CIEF) N36, March 1994

CIRIA, 1995, *A client's guide to greener construction.* CIRIA Special Publication 120 (ISBN 0 86017 423 9)

CIRIA, 1995, *Remedial treatment for contaminated land.*
Volume II – decommissioning, decontamination and demolition, CIRIA Special Publication 102 (ISBN 0 86017 397 6)
Volume III – site investigation and assessment. CIRIA Special Publication 103 (ISBN 0 86017 398 4)
Volume IV – classification and selection of remedial methods. CIRIA Special Publication 104 (ISBN 0 86017 399 2)
Volume V – excavation and disposal. CIRIA Special Publication 105 (ISBN 0 86017 400 X)
Volume VII – ex-situ remedial methods for soils, sludges and sediments. CIRIA Special Publication 107 (ISBN 0 86017 402 6)
Volume VIII – ex-situ remedial methods for contaminated groundwater and other liquids. CIRIA Special Publication 108 (ISBN 0 86017 403 4)
Volume IX – in-situ methods of remediation. CIRIA Special Publication 109 (ISBN 0 86017 404 2)
Volume X – special situations. CIRIA Special Publication 110 (ISBN 0 86017 405 0)
Volume XI – planning and management. CIRIA Special Publication 111 (ISBN 0 86017 406 9)

CIRIA, 1995, *Waste minimisation and recycling in construction – a review.* CIRIA Special Publication 122 (ISBN 0 86017 428 X)

CIRIA, 1996, *Building a cleaner future.* CIRIA Special Publication 141V (joint CIRIA and Environment Agency pack, including training video, booklet and poster)

CIRIA, 1996, *Remedial treatment for contaminated land. Volume VI – containment and hydraulic measures.* CIRIA Special Publication 106 (ISBN 0 86017 401 8)

CIRIA, 1997, *Remedial treatment for contaminated land. Volume XII – Policy and legislation.* CIRIA Special Publication 112 (ISBN 0 86017 407 7)

CIRIA, 1998, *Managing materials and components on site.* CIRIA Special Publication 146 (ISBN 0 86017 481 6)

CIRIA, 1998, *Remedial treatment for contaminated land. Volume 1 – introduction and guide.* CIRIA Special Publication 101 (ISBN 0 86017 396 8)

CIRIA, 1998, *Sewerage system management – scoping study.* CIRIA Project Report 67 (ISBN 0 86017 867 6)

CIRIA, 1998, *Waste minimisation and recycling in construction – training pack,* CIRIA Special Publication 148 (ISBN 0 86017 488 3) containing CIRIA, 1997, *Waste minimisation in construction – site guide.* CIRIA Special Publication 133 (ISBN 0 86017 482 4) video, overheads and disk

CIRIA, 1999, *Environmental good practice on site.* CIRIA Publication C502 (ISBN 0 86017 502 2), comes with poster CIRIA Publication C502P

CIRIA, 1999, *Environmental good practice – working on site.* CIRIA Publication C503 (ISBN 0 86017 503 0)

CIRIA, 1999, *Environmental issues in construction – a desk study.* CIRIA Project Report 73 (ISBN 0 86017 873 0)

CIRIA, 1999, *The observational method in ground engineering – principles and applications.* CIRIA Report 185 (ISBN 0 86017 497 2)

CIRIA, 1999, *The reclaimed and recycled construction materials handbook.* CIRIA Publication C513 (ISBN 0 86017 513 8)

CIRIA, 2000, *Environmental handbook for building and civil engineering projects: Part 1, Design and specification.* CIRIA Publication C512, (ISBN 0 86017 512 X) *Part 2, Construction phase.* CIRIA Publication C528 (ISBN 0 86017 528 6) *Part 3, Demolition and site clearance.* CIRIA Publication C529 (ISBN 0 86017 529 4)

CIRIA, 2000, *Sustainable urban drainage systems – design manual for Scotland and Northern Ireland,* CIRIA Publication C521 (ISBN 0 86017 521 9)

CIRIA, 2000, *Sustainable urban drainage systems – design manual for England and Wales,* CIRIA Publication C522 (ISBN 0 86017 522 7)

Department of the Environment, 1997, *Contaminated land research report no 12, A quality approach for contaminated land consultancy*

Department of the Environment/Welsh Office, 1990, *EC Directive on the protection of groundwater against pollution caused by certain dangerous substances (80/68/EEC): Classification of listed substances.* London: HMSO (ISBN 0 11 752344 5)

Department of the Environment/Welsh Office, 1990, *Water and the environment – the implementation of European Community directives on pollution caused by certain dangerous substances discharged into the aquatic environment.* London: HMSO (ISBN 0 11752 184 1)

Environment Agency, Environment and Heritage, and SEPA pollution prevention guidelines (PPGs):

- PPG1 – *General guide to the prevention of pollution of controlled waters*
- PPG2 – *Above ground oil storage tanks*
- PPG3 – *The use and design of oil separators in surface water drainage systems*
- PPG4 – *Disposal of sewage where no mains drainage is available*
- PPG5 – *Works in, near or liable to affect watercourses*
- PPG6 – *Working at demolition and construction sites*

- PPG7 – *Fuelling stations: construction and operation*
- PPG8 – *Safe storage and disposal of used oils*
- PPG9 – *Pesticides*
- PPG10 – *Highway depots*
- PPG11 – *Industrial sites*
- PPG12 – *Sheep dip*
- PPG13 – *The use of high pressure water and stream cleaners*
- PPG14 – *Boats and marinas*
- PPG15 – *Retail premises*
- PPG16 – *Schools and other educational establishments*
- PPG17 – *Dairies and other milk handling operations*
- PPG18 – *Control of spillages and fire fighting runoff*
- PPG19 – *Garages and vehicle service centres*
- PPG20 – *Dewatering underground ducts and chambers*
- PPG21 – *Metal recycling sites*
- PPG22 – *Dealing with spillages on highways*
- PPG23 – *Maintenance of structures over water*
- PPG24 – *Stables, kennels and catteries*
- PPG25 – *Hospitals and health care establishments*

Environmental agencies/CIRIA technical guidelines (available from EA regional offices):
- Masonry bunds for oil storage tanks
- Concrete bunds for oil storage tanks

Institution of Chemical Engineers, 1992, *Model form of conditions for process plant – Suitable for reimbursable contracts.* Rugby: Institution of Chemical Engineers (ISBN 0 85295 291 0)

Institution of Civil Engineers, 1973 5th edition, *Conditions of contract.* London: Thomas Telford (ISBN 0 7277 0337 4)

Institution of Civil Engineers, 1988 6th edition, *Conditions of contract.* London: Thomas Telford (ISBN 0 7277 1617 4)

Institution of Civil Engineers, 1995 2nd edition, *Conditions of contract for minor works.* London: Thomas Telford (ISBN 0 7277 2037 6)

Institution of Civil Engineers, 1995 2nd edition, *Engineering and construction contract (ECC).* London: Thomas Telford (ISBN 0 7277 2094 5)

Institute of Hydrology, 1999, *Flood estimation handbook*

Maitland, P S and Campbell, R N, 1992, *Freshwater fishes of the British Isles.* London: Harper Collins

SEPA, 1996, *Protecting the quality of Scotland's environment. A guide to surface water best management practices for the protection of groundwater*

SEPA, 1997, *A guide to sustainable urban drainage*

SEPA, 1999, *Development on greenfield sites* (available from SEPA website)

SEPA, 1999, *Guidance for the use and disposal of oil* (available from SEPA website)

SEPA, 1999, *Improving Scotland's water environment* (available from SEPA website)

SEPA, 1999, *Toxic chemicals in the aquatic environment* (available from SEPA website)

Appendices: consent pro forma

DEPARTMENT of the ENVIRONMENT

Water Act (Northern Ireland) 1972

APPLICATION FOR CONSENT

FOR OFFICIAL USE

Date of receipt:

File reference no:

Before completing this form read the notes overleaf

ANSWER HERE

1. NAME AND ADDRESS OF APPLICANT:
   (BLOCK CAPITALS)

   Telephone No:

2. NAME AND ADDRESS OF AGENT (if any):
   (BLOCK CAPITALS)

   Telephone No:

3. ADDRESS OF PREMISES FROM WHICH
   EFFLUENT ORIGINATES:

4. TRADE CONDUCTED ON PREMISES:

5. DETAILS OF PROCESS, OPERATION OR OTHER SOURCE
   FROM WHICH TRADE EFFLUENT ORIGINATES:

6. DESCRIPTION OF TRADE EFFLUENT PLANT:

7. NUMBER OF TRADE EFFLUENT DISCHARGE POINTS:

8. NATURE OF ANY SEPARATE DISCHARGE:
   (EG: COOLING WATER, SEWAGE)

[P.T.O.

1

9. NATURE AND COMPOSITION OF EFFLUENT:
   (average composition and range of variation)

    (i) Biochemical Oxygen Demand (5 days)

   (ii) Suspended Solids (mg/litre)

  (iii) pH Value

  (iv) Maximum temperature (°C)

   (v) Maximum quantity on any one day (m^3 day)

  (vi) Maximum rate of flow (litres per second)

 (vii) Chemicals (give concentration if possible)

(viii) Any other poisonous, noxious or
      polluting component:

  (ix) Other relevant information:

10. DESCRIPTION AND QUANTITY OF CHEMICALS AND OIL
    STORED ON PREMISES:

I/WE HEREBY make application for the consent of the Department of the Environment to make a discharge of trade effluent into a waterway referred to and located on the enclosed site plan.

Signed ....

For and on behalf of ....

Date ....

2

NOTES

Under the terms of Section 7 of the Water Act (NI) 1972 the consent of the Department of the Environment is required to the discharge of any trade or sewage effluent or any poisonous, noxious or polluting matter into a waterway.

"WATERWAY" means any river, stream, watercourse, inland water (whether natural or artificial) or tidal waters, but does not include any public sewer.

"TRADE EFFLUENT" means any liquid, either with or without particles of matter in suspension therein, which is discharged from premises used for carrying on any trade or industry, other than storm water or domestic sewage.

A SEPARATE APPLICATION must be completed in respect of each discharge: if the sewage or cooling water effluent from your premises is discharged separately to a waterway, individual application is required in each case.

EACH APPLICATION must be accompanied by a SITE PLAN showing:-

(a)   the location of the treatment plant,

(b)   the effluent sampling point and access thereto,

(c)   the exact location of the outlet or discharge point.

ON COMPLETION THIS FORM SHOULD BE RETURNED TO:

Department of the Environment
Environmental Protection
Calvert House
23 Castle Place
BELFAST
BT1 1FY

3   CPU 22463 1(m) 3/92 CSSY

A2 Abstraction licence, England and Wales – Part A

WR1 Part A Water abstraction and impoundment – Application for a licence

For Environment Agency use only	Application reference number	Computer reference

ENVIRONMENT AGENCY

Water abstraction and impoundment
Application for a licence

Part A

Environment Act 1995, Water Resources Act 1991,
Water Resources (Licences) Regulations 1965

Everyone has to fill in Part A of the form
Please read the notes on how to fill in the forms

For Environment Agency use only

Proposal

☐ Part B of this form
☐ Part C of this form

Date first received

Date acknowledged informally

Date application valid

Date of statutory acknowledgment

Date determination due by

Date determined

Fee received

Receipt number

Comments

A1 Type of application

A1.1 Please tell us about the type of application you are making.
Are you applying

☐ for a new licence to abstract water? *please fill in Part A and Part B*

☐ to vary an existing licence to abstract water? *please fill in Part A and Part B*

☐ to impound water or alter an existing impounding works? *please fill in Part A and Part C*

☐ to create an impounding works and then abstract water? *please fill in Parts A, B and C.*

A2 The applicant

A2.1 Please give the full name and address of the person or organisation applying for the licence.

If you are applying on behalf of a partnership or other organisation, please read the notes which came with this form about answering this question.

If you need to give more than one name and address, put the first or trading name of the firm and use a separate sheet for the rest.

Name

Address

Postcode

Contact numbers

Phone

Fax

A2 The applicant *continued*

A2.2 Do you want to nominate someone we can contact for queries about your application?

No ☐ *we will address all questions and correspondence to the applicant named in section A2.1*

Yes ☐ *please give details*

We will send all the correspondence about your licence to the person you name here.

Name

Address

Postcode

Contact numbers

Phone

Fax

A3 Statutory notices

A3.1 Do you need to issue a public notice?

Please read the separate notes about Public Notices N1–N4

No ☐ *go to 'A4 Environmental appraisal'*

Yes ☐ *please complete this section*

A3.2 When and where was the notice published?

Please enclose original pages from the newspapers.

Name of newspaper

Date of first publication

Date of second publication

A3.3 When was the notice published in the London Gazette?

You do not need to send us a copy of this.

Date

A3.4 When was the application made available for public inspection?

Start date

End date

A3 Statutory notices *continued*

A3.5 Where was the application made available for public inspection?

Statutory authorities

Please say when you served notice on any statutory authorities.

A3.6 Have you served notice on the Internal Drainage Board (IDB)?

No ☐ *(not required)*

Yes ☐ *please give details*

Date

Name of IDB

A3.7 Have you served notice on the Navigation Authority?

No ☐ *(not required)*

Yes ☐ *please give details*

Date

Name of Authority

A3.8 Have you served notice on the Harbour Authority?

No ☐ *(not required)*

Yes ☐ *please give details*

Date

Name of Authority

A3.9 Have you served notice on the Conservancy Authority?

No ☐ *(not required)*

Yes ☐ *please give details*

Date

Name of Authority

A3.10 Have you served notice on the Water Undertaker?

No ☐ *(not required)*

Yes ☐ *please give details*

Date

Name of Water Undertaker

A4 Environmental appraisal

A4.1 Do you need to do an environmental appraisal?

If you have not already talked to us about whether you need to do this, or in some cases a formal 'Environmental assessment', please get in touch with us now.

No ☐

Yes ☐ *Please enclose a copy of the environmental information with this application form.*

A5 Checklist

A5.1 Please read through this list and tick the items you are sending us with this application.

☐ Part B of this form

☐ Part C of this form

☐ Notices of proposals to impound and/or abstract water as they appeared in local newspapers *we need original full pages from the newspapers – do not send copies*

☐ An environmental report

☐ A map of the site showing all the required details

☐ Continuation sheets for answers to question

A5.2 Fees

Please tick all that apply

☐ I enclose the correct fee for processing this application Please make cheques payable to the 'Environment Agency'

☐ Please send a receipt

☐ The Environment Agency has told me I do not have to pay an application fee

A6 Application and declaration

It is an offence to make a false statement when applying for a licence.

I declare that to the best of my knowledge the statements made in the application forms, including the map and any accompanying sheets, are true.

I apply to the Environment Agency to

☐ abstract water from an inland water

☐ abstract water from underground strata

☐ impede the flow of an inland water by means of impounding works

☐ vary licence number

Signature

Name

Position

Date

Data Protection Act Notice

1. "The Environment Agency is responsible for regulating environmental protection, flood defence, water resources and fisheries. It has a duty to discharge its functions to protect and enhance the environment and to promote conservation and recreation".

2. The information you give will be used by the Environment Agency to process your application. It will be placed on the relevant public register(s), and used to monitor compliance with licence conditions, or to process renewal applications.

3. We may also use and/or disclose any of the information you give us in order to:
    *   offer/provide you with our literature/services relating to environmental matters
    *   consult with the public, public bodies and other organisations (e.g. Health and Safety Executive, Local Authorities, emergency services, MAFF, English Nature on environmental issues),
    *   carry out statistical analysis, research and development on environmental issues
    *   provide public register information to enquirers
    *   investigate possible breaches of environmental law and taking any resulting action
    *   prevent breaches of environmental law
    *   assess customer service satisfaction and improve our service

    We may pass on the information to agents/representatives who we ask to do any of these things on our behalf.

4. Individuals have a right to see the information we hold about them. We will correct it if it is inaccurate.

Part B

For Environment Agency use only   Application reference number   Computer reference

ENVIRONMENT AGENCY

Application for a licence to abstract water

Part B

Environment Act 1995, Water Resources Act 1991,
Water Resources (Licences) Regulations 1965

Only use this part if you want
- **a new licence to abstract water**
- **to create an impounding reservoir and abstract water from it**
- **to vary an existing licence.**

B1 Applicant's name

This should be the same name as in answer to Part A question A2.1

B2 Type of application

B2.1 Are you applying

☐ for a new licence to abstract water? *go to 'B3 Location of abstraction'*

☐ to create an impounding reservoir and abstract water from it? *go to 'B3 Location of abstraction'.*

☐ to vary an existing licence?

Varying the licence

B2.2 Are you the licence holder?

No ☐ *please get in touch with us*

Yes ☐ *please give details and tell us about the changes you want to make in the box opposite. Please enclose the licence with this application.*

Licence number

Date issued

B2 Type of application *continued*

The changes you want to make

Form WR1 Part B   page 1

B3 Location of abstraction

Please send us a map showing each point or between which points you intend to abstract water from.

To help us locate the points you intend to abstract water from, please use the table below to tell us

- the National Grid Reference *please give an eight-figure reference number if you can*
- the name of the inland water *if you do not know the name please give a description, for example, 'tributary of River X'*
- the address of the site *give postal address, local name or description of the site*
- how you have labelled each point on the map *for example, 'A', 'B' etc.*
- for underground strata, please tell us the strata type from which the water will be extracted *for example, 'chalk'*

B3.1 Inland water

Name of point 1

Site address	National Grid Reference
	Map label

Name of point 2

Site address	National Grid Reference
	Map label

Name of point 3

Site address	National Grid Reference
	Map label

Name of point 4

Site address	National Grid Reference
	Map label

B3.2 Underground strata

Name of point 1	Strata type

Site address	National Grid Reference
	Map label

Name of point 2	Strata type

Site address	National Grid Reference
	Map label

Continues

page 2

Form WR1 Part B

B3 Location of abstraction *continued*

Name of point 3

Strata type

Site address

National Grid Reference

Map label

Name of point 4

Strata type

Site address

National Grid Reference

Map label

B4 Entitlement to apply

Please read the notes which came with this form before answering this question.

B4.1 Are you the occupier or potential occupier?

We need to know if you are the occupier or potential occupier of

- the land adjoining the inland water
- the land which comprises the underground strata

If you have different rights for different sites, please give details on a separate sheet.

☐ Occupier
☐ Expect to occupy from

B4.2 Do you have, or expect to have, rights of access?

This question applies only if your application is for abstraction from an inland water.

If you do not occupy the land adjoining the inland water, you may still apply for a licence providing you have a right of access to the inland water or will have such a right when we come to issue a licence.

If you have different rights for different sites, please give details on a separate sheet.

☐ Have right of access
☐ Expect to have right of access from

B4.3 How have you marked the map you have enclosed to show

- the land you occupy or will occupy
- the land you have or will have right of access to?

For example, 'outlined in red'.

B5 Duration of licence

B5.1 How long do you want the licence to last?

☐ Indefinitely *please note that, even so, we may set a time limit*
☐ For a limited time *please give dates*
From

To

B5.2 Would the licence be linked to a particular project?

No ☐
Yes ☐ How long is the project due to last?
   ☐ Indefinitely
   ☐ For a limited time *please give dates*
   From

   To

B6 Abstraction details

B6.1 Please give us details about the abstraction.

Please specify
- the maximum quantity of water you want to abstract for each purpose
- where you will abstract it from
- where you intend to use the water
- when you intend to abstract it.

Purpose	Where will you abstract the water?	Where will you use the water?	When do you plan to abstract it? *Please be specific*
Public water supply			
Domestic water supply			
Private water supply			
Spray irrigation			
Agriculture or horticulture (other than spray irrigation)			
Watercress growing			
Fish farm			
Mineral washing			
Hydropower			
Industry or commercial: Process water			
Industry or commercial: Evaporative cooling			
Industry or commercial: Non-evaporative cooling			
Other *please specify*			

B7 Spray irrigation of crops

You must answer this question if you intend to use water for spray irrigation.

	Type of crop or other to be irrigated	Period of irrigation	Area of crop *in hectares*	Maximum amount of water to be used during the specified period *in millimetres*	What is the total number of hectares you intend to irrigate in any one day?
Crop/use 1					
Crop/use 2					
Crop/use 3					

Form WR1 Part B

CIRIA C532

Amount of water you intend to abstract

Maximum yearly in m^3	Maximum daily in m^3	Maximum hourly in m^3	Hours per day	Peak instantaneous flow rate in l/s

Other

Total	Total	Total	Total	Total

Form WR1 Part B

B8 Method and measurement of abstraction

B8.1 For each point of abstraction, we need to know

- the type, capacity and number of pumps (or other forms of intake equipment)
- the measurement method you will use *for example, meter*
- whether you have applied for intake works consent *please give details and reference for that application.*

Please use separate sheets if you need to.

Map label	Machinery/works	Measurement method	Intake consent

B9 Abstraction from underground strata

B9.1 Do the works include headings or adits?

No ☐

Yes ☐ *please give details*

Point of communication	Length	Diameter	Orientation

B9.2 Have you had a groundwater investigation on this site?

A groundwater investigation will usually be necessary.

No ☐ *please contact us before proceeding further*

Yes ☐ *please give the consent reference number*

[   ]

B9.3 Please give us details about boreholes, wells, etc.

We need to know

- the size and depth of each well, borehole, etc.
- if it will be lined, the type of lining or linings
- how you intend to prevent leakage or overflow from any artesian works.

Map label	Depth *in metres*	Diameter *in millimetres*	Lining	How will overflow or leakage be prevented from artesian works?

page 6

Form WR1 Part B

B10 Other considerations

B10.1 Have you asked a water company for a supply for any of the purposes listed in question B6.1?

No ☐ *go to question B10.2*

Yes ☐ *please give details*

Purpose you wanted water for

Company you applied to

Date you applied

Result of application

B10.2 Are any of the abstraction point(s) in this application already licensed or in another application?

No ☐ *go to question B10.3*

Yes ☐ *please give details*

Name and address of site

Postcode

National Grid Reference

Serial number of licence (or date you applied for it)

B10.3 Will you store abstracted water on your land?

No ☐

Yes ☐ *please say how*

B10.4 How much of the water you abstract will be re-used?

B10.5 How have you calculated the quantities you need to abstract?

Please send us details of your calculations.

B10.6 How do you make best use of your existing water supplies?

B10 Other considerations *continued*

Discharging used water from the site

We need to know what will happen to any water you discharge from the site. *If you are abstracting water for more than one purpose, please give us details for each purpose on a separate sheet.*

B10.7 Do you intend to discharge used water from the site?

No ☐ *go to 'B11 Checklist'*

Yes ☐

B10.8 Do you have a consent from the Environment Agency to discharge water from this site?

Include permission you got from the old NRA or water authority.

No ☐

Yes ☐ *please give the consent reference number*

B10.9 What proportion of water will be discharged after use?

☐ %

B10.10 Where will it be discharged?

Please give details such as 'public sewer', 'inland water'. Please mark the discharge points on the map.

B11 Checklist

B11.1 Please read through this list and tick the items you are sending us with this application.

☐ The existing licence you want to vary (if applicable)

☐ Proof of right to occupy or have access to the site

☐ Details of how you calculated the amount of water you intend to abstract

☐ Continuation sheets for answers to question(s)

Map *This should show*

☐ each point of abstraction marked

☐ the area of land over which you have rights of access marked

☐ the area(s) of land on which the water is to be used marked

☐ the site of any proposed reservoir marked

☐ the point(s) where used water will be discharged marked.

For applications from water undertakers

☐ We need to know how the discharged water will affect the water infrastructure in the area. *You may need to enclose separate information from local water or sewerage companies.*

Form WR1 Part B

page 7

Part C

For Environment Agency use only

Application reference number

Computer reference

ENVIRONMENT AGENCY

Application for a licence to impound water

Part C

Environment Act 1995, Water Resources Act 1991,
Water Resources (Licences) Regulations 1965

Only use this part if all you propose is impoundment

C1 Applicant's name

This should be the same name as in answer to Part A question A2.1

C2 Type of application

C2.1 Is this application for new impounding works?

No ☐

Yes ☐ *go to 'C3 Location of impounding works'*

C2.2 Are you applying to alter existing impounding works?

No ☐

Yes ☐ *are the impounding works already licensed?*

    No ☐ *go to question C2.4*

    Yes ☐

C2 Type of application *continued*

C2.3 Please give us details about the current licence.

Licence number

Licence issued by

C2.4 Do any other statutory provisions apply to the site?

No ☐

Yes ☐ *please say what they are*

C3 Location of impounding works

To help us locate the site you intend to impound, please use the table below to tell us

- the National Grid Reference
- the name (if any) and location of the river or watercourse
- the address of the site (give postal address, local name or description of the site)
- how you have labelled each point on the map (for example 'A', 'B' etc.)

C3.1 Inland water

Name of point 1

Site address

National Grid Reference

Map label

Name of point 2

Site address

National Grid Reference

Map label

Continues

C3 Location of impounding site *continued*

Name of point 3

Site address

National Grid Reference

Map label

Name of point 4

Site address

National Grid Reference

Map label

C4 Description of impounding works

C4.1 Please give us details about your proposals.

Please

- give a full description of your proposals to alter or develop impounding works
- send us plans and sections of your proposals for the impounding works.

Continue on separate sheets if you need to.

C4.2 Will any areas be submerged?

No ☐

Yes ☐ *please show these areas on the map*

Form WR1 Part C

CIRIA C532

C4 Description of impounding works *cont.*

C4.3 Will the impounded area be lined?

No ☐

Yes ☐ *please say how*

[ ]

How the water will be used

C4.4 Will the impounding works be used to regulate the flow of another inland water?

No ☐

Yes ☐ *please give details*

Name of inland water

[ ]

How marked on map

[ ]

C4.5 Will the impounding reservoir be used as a source of water?

No ☐

Yes ☐ *please give details*

How the water will be used?

[ ]

Maximum daily rate

[cubic metres]

Maximum yearly rate

[cubic metres]

How the works will provide this yield *continue on a separate sheet if you need to.*

[ ]

Please give us details of any other way you intend to use the water you impound *for example, to create an ornamental lake, fisheries etc.*

[ ]

C5 Flow controls, levels and capacities

Flow controls

C5.1 Do you intend to operate flow controls?

No ☐ *go to question C5.4*

Yes ☐ *please answer the next question*

C5.2 Please give us details about the point of discharge.

Description

[ ]

National Grid Reference

[| | | | | | | | |]

Map label

[ ]

C5.3 Please give us details about the control point for
- maintenance of minimum flow, or
- measurement of prescribed flow.

Description

[ ]

National Grid Reference

[| | | | | | | | |]

Map label

[ ]

Proposed flow at control point

[units:]

Measurement method at control point

[ ]

Levels, capacities etc.

C5.4 What will the planned overflow level of the weir or reservoir be?

Please state by reference to Ordinance Datum (Newlyn).

[metres]

C5.5 Is the planned capacity of the reservoir over 25,000 cubic metres?

Use the capacity when full to spillway level.

No ☐ *please give the capacity*

[cubic metres]

Yes ☐ Will you be creating a raised reservoir?

No ☐ *go to 'C6 Diversion works'*

Yes ☐

C5.6 Have you complied with the Reservoirs Act 1975?

No ☐

Yes ☐

C6 Diversion works

C6.1 Do you intend to divert the flow of the inland water while you are constructing or altering the impounding works?

No ☐

Yes ☐ *please give details of how this will be achieved*

Continue on separate sheets if you need to.

C7 Other formalities

You may need to apply for permission for your works under

- the Water Resources Act 1991 Section 109 *if your works will affect a main river*
- the Water Resources Act 1991 Section 90 *if you intend to use sluices or scour releases*
- Land Drainage Act 1991 Section 23 *if your works would affect the flow of any watercourse, (other than a main river).*

Please get in touch with us if you need to know how these Acts affect your application.

C7.1 Do you need to apply for consent under any of these Acts?

No ☐ *please go to section 'C8 Checklist'*

Yes ☐ *Have you already applied for consent under any of these Acts?*

    No ☐ *please go to 'C8 Checklist'*

    Yes ☐ *please give details*

Water Resources Act 1991 Section 109

Date you applied

Reference number

Details of application

Water Resources Act 1991 Section 90

Date you applied

Reference number

Details of application

C7 Other formalities *continued*

Land Drainage Act 1991 Section 23

Date you applied

Reference number

Details of application

C8 Checklist

C8.1 Please read through this list and check the items you are sending us with the application.

☐ Plans and sections of the proposed impounding works

☐ Calculations for the maximum quantities you gave in answer to question C4

☐ Continuation sheets for answers to question(s)

Map *This should show*

☐ the location of impounding works marked

☐ areas to be submerged marked

☐ the points where used water will be discharged marked

☐ control point for maintaining or measuring flow marked

page 4

Form WR1 Part C

CIRIA C532

Guidance notes

ENVIRONMENT AGENCY

Water resources

Application for a licence to abstract and impound water

Guidance notes

Glossary

The following definitions are derived from the Water Resources Act 1991. They are believed accurate, but the Act contains the definitive text.

Abstraction

'Abstraction' means removing water from a source of supply (temporarily or permanently). It includes water removed for transfer to another source of supply.

Discrete waters

'Discrete waters' are any inland water (such as a lake, pond or reservoir), which does not discharge into any other inland water. They can also be a group of two or more lakes, ponds or reservoirs (including watercourses or mains connecting them) which do not discharge into any inland water outside the group.

Discrete waters are not a 'source of supply' for the purposes of the Water Resources Act 1991 and an abstraction licence is not needed.

Impounding works

'Impounding Works' means (i) any dam, weir, or other works in an inland water which allows water to be impounded, and (ii) any works for diverting the flow of an inland water in connection with the construction or alteration of any dam, weir or other works falling within (i).

Inland water

'Inland Waters' are

- any natural or artificial river, stream or other watercourse whether tidal or not
- any natural or artificial lake or pond
- any reservoir or dock
- any other channel, creek, bay, estuary or arm of the sea.

Source of supply

A 'source of supply' is any inland water (except discrete waters) or any underground strata in which water can be contained.

Underground strata

'Underground strata' means strata subjacent to the surface of any land. Water in 'underground strata' includes water contained in

- a well, borehole, or works ancillary to these
- any excavation into underground strata where the level of water depends on entry of water from those strata.

It does not include water in

- a sewer, pipe, reservoir, tank
- any other underground works constructed in underground strata (where the water is not in contact with water in the strata).

Watercourses

The term 'Watercourse' includes all rivers, streams, ditches, drains, cuts, culverts, dykes, sluices, sewers and passages through which water flows, except mains and other pipes used for the purpose only of providing a supply of water to any premises, local authority sewers, adits and passages treated as contained in underground strata.

Part A   Questions A1–A6

A1 Type of application

You need to fill in an application form for a licence for

- new abstractions
- new impoundments

and also

- to vary an existing abstraction licence
- to alter existing impounding works.

Licence variations

If you want to make any changes (variations) to a licence **you already hold**, you usually have to apply to us for a new licence. This is because the process is governed by strict, formal rules. Also, in practice, variations can have effects which are not immediately obvious. However, if you are proposing to reduce the amount of water you are licensed to abstract, or require a very minor change, we have a simpler form. If you have occupied land which an existing licence covers, please contact us as special rules apply.

We can advise you on the appropriate procedure and which forms to use.

A2 The applicant

If the applicant is

- an individual, give their first names and surname
- a company, give the address of the Registered Office
- a firm or partnership, give
  - full names and addresses of all partners
  - the trading name
  - its trading address
- a club or charity, give
  - the full names and addresses of all trustees
  - the name and address of the person authorised to receive the Licence on their behalf.

You should also give us the name and address if you have nominated someone different (for example, an agent) as contact for this application.

A3 Statutory notices

Usually you will have to publicise this application. **If so it is essential that the requirements are fully complied with,** otherwise the proposal may need to be re-advertised. Requirements include placing advertisements, serving notices on certain bodies, and making the application available for public inspection. We do however have a discretion whether to require this in cases of abstractions of not more than 20 cubic meters per day, so if you are planning such an abstraction, ask us before going through this procedure. Full details of the procedure are set out on the back of the Notice forms, N1 to N4.

A4 Environmental appraisal

Abstraction of water or impounding works, or the project of which these form a part, may have environmental effects which require appraisal. Unless these are negligible, some appraisal of these is required to be made in an 'Environmental report'.

In cases where **significant** environmental effects are likely, a formal environmental assessment may be required by European law. This requires an 'Environmental statement', which is a more elaborate 'Environmental report' which must cover particular points, but also with an emphasis on careful consideration of environmental aspects of the proposal from the very beginning. Alternatively, the water-related information may be in an Environmental statement which already exists (or is planned) if the proposal is part of a project where a statement has been asked for by, for example, a planning authority. Please contact us to discuss what is needed.

A5 Map (Checklist)

You must send a map with this application. If you are applying to impound and abstract water you can use the same map for both parts of the application. But please make sure that all the information is shown clearly, and

- use an Ordnance Survey map on a scale of 1:10,000 (approximately 6 inches to 1 mile) or larger
- use an A4 sheet to reproduce the area of land covered by your application
- label individual points and areas ('A', 'B' and so on)
- use colouring or hatching to highlight areas on the map
- use the form to cross-refer to labelled and highlighted areas on the map.

It may be easier to explain or clarify complicated proposals (including answering questions on the forms) by reference to maps and plans than in words.

A6 Application and declaration

It will help us if you are as open and accurate as possible when you make your application. However, please note that in any case it is a criminal offence to

- make false statements in order to obtain a licence
- impound or abstract water without a licence where one is necessary
- fail to comply with conditions on a licence
- fail to provide us with information about an abstraction whether licensable or not
- interfere with meters or other devices to measure quantities of water abstracted.

If you are convicted, you could be fined or sent to prison, or both.

Officers of corporate bodies may be personally liable under Sections 206 and 217 of the Water Resources Act 1991.

Part B Questions B1–B11

B2 Type of application

If you are applying to vary an existing licence to abstract water, summarise the changes you are applying for.

When you complete the rest of the application form, show the total you now wish to have licensed.

For example

- if you want to increase the quantities of water you are licensed to abstract, give the new maximum quantities required, not the quantity you want them increased by
- if you want to abstract water from additional points show the existing abstraction points as well as the new ones.

B3 Location of abstraction

If you are not sure exactly where you will abstract from an inland water

- give the National Grid References of the points between which you plan to abstract, and bracket them together
- label the points with letter(s), ('A', 'B' and so on).

If the inland water or underground source has a local name please give it.

B4 Entitlement to apply

We can only consider an application for a licence to abstract water from someone who is legally entitled to apply for one.

Occupier or potential occupier

We will consider your application if at the proposed abstraction point(s) you are

- the occupier of land adjoining the inland water or which comprises the underground strata from which you propose to abstract
- a potential occupier (for example, if you are negotiating to become an occupier or have started compulsory purchase procedures).

Rights of access

You may also apply to abstract from an inland water if you have a right of access or expect to have a right of access to the land directly adjoining the inland water.

Rights of access are not sufficient where the proposed abstraction is from underground strata, except where water contained in an excavation is treated as contained in underground strata.

If you are a potential occupier or expect to have a right of access you must be able to prove your potential rights. Either

- send us evidence about your prospective occupation or right of access
- summarise on a separate sheet what that evidence is.

We may ask to see proof such as the title deeds, tenancy agreements etc.

B5 Duration of licence

Even if you have applied for an indefinite licence, the licence will usually be granted to expire on a specified date.

Licences cannot be renewed, so if you wish to abstract water after the specified date, you must apply for a new one.

You should any way not apply for an indefinite licence if the duration of your project is limited (for example, by the duration of a lease or planning permission).

B6 Abstraction details

We need these details to help decide if the quantity you plan to abstract or impound is reasonable for your needs.

Information we need in the individual columns is explained below.

How we work out what you have to pay for the water you abstract

How much we charge depends on
- the amount of water you are licensed to abstract
- the source of the water
- the time of the year you abstract the water
- the purpose the water is used for.

You may find it cheaper to restrict the water you abstract, or when you use it, according to the season.

There is more about this in our Annual abstraction charges scheme *leaflet. Please get in touch with us if you need a copy.*

Purpose

If the water is required for industrial or commercial use, please say what the business is and how the water will be used, distinguishing between different uses.

Year/period quantity

State the maximum amount (cubic metres) of water you propose to abstract per year or during the specified period for each purpose.
- Daily quantity
  For each purpose – give the maximum amount of water you propose to abstract in any one day (in cubic metres). This could be more than the yearly quantity divided by the number of days.
- Hourly rate
  For each purpose – give the maximum amount (cubic metres) of water you propose to abstract in any one hour, and for how many hours per day.
- Peak instantaneous flow rate
  For each purpose – give the maximum rate (in litres per second) that you plan to abstract at any given moment.

Where you will abstract the water

For each purpose
- state 'S' (surface water, ie. inland waters) or 'G' (groundwater)
- give the label you have used on the map ('A', 'B', and so on).

B6 Abstraction details *continued*

Where you will use the water

For each purpose say
- where water will be used
- how that place/area is marked on the map.
  Use separate shadings, numberings etc.

If you are a statutory water undertaker or a private water supplier

You do not need to state the precise location of use, but it will help us to process the application if you give as much information as possible.

Where water is used to supply properties for 'domestic use' or 'private water supply' you should
- identify individual properties
- specify how you propose to use the water (for example, own family, tied cottage, another private family, holiday cottage, guest house and so on).

B7 Spray irrigation of crops

Spray irrigation is usually for agricultural use, but can be for other purposes, including frost protection, golf courses, sports fields and racehorse gallops. This section must be completed to justify a reasonable need for the total quantities for which you are applying.

B8 Method and measurement of abstraction

We need to know how you propose to
- abstract the water
- measure how much you are abstracting.

Please give full details of the works and equipment involved, with any drawings available.

If you plan to abstract more than 20 cubic metres a day, you will have to install a suitable meter or use some other means of measurement.

We can give you advice about what sort of meter to install. Occasionally, we may ask you to install a meter for quantities of less than 20 cubic metres a day.

For intake works on watercourses

You may also need a consent under
- the Water Resources Act 1991, Section 109
- the Land Drainage Act 1991, Section 23.

Please get in touch with us if you need more information.

Section 109 applies to any structures which
- is in a watercourse which is part of the 'main river'
- divert the flood waters of the main river.

You should check with us to see whether the watercourse in question is a 'main river' or not.

Section 23 applies if your works affect or obstruct the flow of any watercourse, other than a main river.

Where the watercourse is controlled by an Internal Drainage Board (IDB), it will deal with the consent. Otherwise, please get in touch with us.

B10.7– B10.10 Discharging used water from the site

We need to know
- how much of the abstracted water will be discharged after use
- the point(s) where the water will enter an inland water, a public sewer, a soakaway, etc. *Describe the point(s) as clearly as possible on this form and mark it/them ('P', 'Q', and so on) on the map.*

Water undertakers should indicate (continue on a separate sheet if you need to) how the abstraction is likely to affect the sewerage infrastructure in the area.
The discharge may need consent from us (in relation to pollution control).

Part C   Questions C1–C8

C4 Description of impounding works

Describe the impounding works in as much detail as possible. Include
- details of what you propose to construct
- details of any existing works and the proposed alterations
- how the works will affect the flow of the inland water.

We also need to see plans and sections
- drawn by a competent engineer or surveyor
- with levels shown to Ordnance Datum (Newlyn).

C5 Flow controls, levels and capacities

Most impounding schemes need a means of controlling and monitoring flows downstream. We need to agree appropriate flow control arrangements with you.

If you do not intend to operate flow controls
- leave this question blank
- we will get in touch if we think that flow controls are necessary.

Levels, capacities

You must inform your County Council or Unitary Council if the work you plan will create a reservoir which holds more than 25,000 cubic metres of water which is above the natural level of the lowest point on the adjoining land.
The Reservoirs Act 1975 applies to such reservoirs.

C6 Diversion works

Please include plans and drawings.

C7 Other formalities

You may also need a consent under
- the Water Resources Act 1991, Section 109
- the Land Drainage Act 1991, Section 23:
Please get in touch with us if you need more information.

Section 109 applies to any structure which
- is in a watercourse which is part of the 'main river'
- divert the flood waters of the main river.

You should check with us to see whether the watercourse in question is a 'main river' or not.

Section 23 applies if your works affect or obstruct the flow of any watercourse, other than a main river.

Where the watercourse is controlled by an Internal Drainage Board (IDB), it will deal with the consent. Otherwise, please get in touch with us.

Scour releases

You will need a consent under Section 90 of the Water Resources Act 1991 to release deposits (scours) accumulated by dams etc. If your impounding works will have sluices which will be opened from time to time resulting in this kind of scouring, please get in touch with us before submitting the application.

Guidance notes for Form WR1 Parts A, B, C

CIRIA C532

A3   Land drainage consent, England and Wales

Environment Act 1995
Land Drainage Act 1991 - Sections 17 or 23
Water Resources Act 1991 - Section 109
Flood Defence (Land Drainage) Byelaws/Sea Defence Byelaws
Highways Act 1980

ENVIRONMENT AGENCY

APPLICATION FOR CONSENT FOR WORKS AFFECTING
WATERCOURSES AND/OR FLOOD DEFENCES

IMPORTANT NOTE. We ask you to read this form and the attached notes before you fill it in. Please take care in answering the questions. If the form is fully and accurately completed, it will ensure as little delay as possible in processing your application. If you have any queries, ask us. **Please complete the form in block letters.**

1   DETAILS OF APPLICANT

NAME:

CONTACT PERSON:

POSTAL ADDRESS:

POSTCODE:

TELEPHONE NO. (Office hours):
TELEPHONE NO. (Out of hours):

FAX NO:

2   AGENTS DETAILS   (eg. Consultant/land agent - if applicable)

NAME: PROFESSION:

POSTAL ADDRESS: CONTACT:
                                 (PERSON DEALING
                                 WITH APPLICATION)

                                 TELEPHONE NO:

POSTCODE: FAX NO:

OFFICIAL USE ONLY   **Thames Region South East Area**

                     YES/NO

MAIN RIVER			DATE APPLICATION RECEIVED:
FEE APPLICABLE			WRA91/LDA91/BYELAW/HA80:
FEE RECEIVED			FILE/OFFICE REFERENCE:

SEnofee.frm.doc NO. FD1

SPECIMEN

3 APPLICANTS INTEREST IN LAND

4 LOCATION

LOCATION OF PROPOSED WORKS:

NAME OF RIVER/WATERCOURSE (if known):

DISTRICT COUNCIL/UNITARY AUTHORITY:

PARISH/COMMUNITY COUNCIL: OS GRID REFERENCE:

5 DESCRIPTION AND PURPOSE OF PROPOSED WORKS

NUMBER OF STRUCTURES

6 DESCRIPTION AND REFERENCE NUMBERS OF ALL PLANS AND SECTIONS SUBMITTED

7 CONSTRUCTION DETAILS

STATE WHETHER WORKS ARE TO BE PERMANENT OR TEMPORARY:

IF TEMPORARY, STATE DURATION REQUIRED:

FOR ALL WORKS STATE ANTICIPATED CONSTRUCTION START DATE:

8 OTHER ENVIRONMENT AGENCY INTERESTS

YES/NO

DO THE PROPOSED WORKS INVOLVE OR AFFECT:-

a)   DISCHARGE OF TRADE EFFLUENT

b)   DISCHARGE OF SURFACE WATER

c)   AN IMPOUNDMENT OF A WATERCOURSE

d)   ABSTRACTION OF WATER

e)   FISH OR FISHERIES

f)   THE DISPOSAL OF WASTE MATERIAL

PLEASE TICK APPROPRIATE BOXES

9 IF PLANNING APPROVAL HAS BEEN GRANTED STATE:

PLANNING AUTHORITY:

APPLICATION NO: APPROVAL DATE:

10 NAME OF PERSON OR ORGANISATION RESPONSIBLE FOR MAINTAINING THE STRUCTURE ON COMPLETION

11 BRIEF DETAILS OF ENVIRONMENTAL IMPACT OF WORKS TOGETHER WITH ANY PROPOSALS FOR AMELIORATION AND/OR COMPENSATORY ENHANCEMENT

12 DECLARATION

I/We:

1   Apply for consent to carry out works as described in this application form and on the attached plan(s).

2   Enclose three copies of suitable plans sufficient to show clearly the location of the proposed works together with three copies of plans and sections showing details of the proposed works to a scale appropriate to the nature of the works and any relevant calculations.

Name: ....

Signed: ....

On behalf of: ....

Date: ....

Please return this form to:

Customer Services
Environment Agency
Swift House
Frimley Business Park
Frimley
Camberley
Surrey
GU16 5SQ

Further information may be obtained from the above office: Telephone No: 01276 454300
Fax No: 01276 454352

ENVIRONMENT AGENCY

WATER RESOURCES ACT 1991 (schedule 10)

(as amended by the Environment Act 1995)

Application for new consent/variation to an existing consent* to discharge

(* delete as appropriate)

Regional/Area Address:	*Official Use Only* *Dist/Area Ref:* *Application No.* *Date Received:* *Fee Received:*

Each applicant must complete the main form and may need to complete a separate annexe if appropriate. Please look through the form and read the notes carefully before you complete it. Processing of your application will be aided by full and accurate completion of all the relevant sections and provision of the necessary plans. If you have any queries regarding the form please contact the person given in the notes.

NOTE:

All information contained within this application will be made available on the public register unless there is a request to withhold any of it. Any such request should provide a full justification stating why the information needs to be withheld

1 SITE ADDRESS

1.1 Address or other sufficient description of land or premises to which this application applies.

Post Code:

2 DETAILS OF DISCHARGE(S)

2.1 State the nature of the discharge(s) (see note i and ii) - tick one or more boxes as appropriate:-

Sewage Effluent - volume of 5 cubic metres per day or less ☐

Sewage Effluent - volume greater than 5 cubic metres per day **(complete annexe 1)** ☐

Sewage Effluent discharged under storm or emergency conditions **(complete annexe 2)** ☐

Cooling Water **(complete annexe 3)** ☐

Trade Effluent *(including site drainage)* **(complete annexe 3)** ☐

Others *(please specify)* ☐

2.2 Please state the maximum quantity it is proposed to discharge in any one day [____] m³/day
Briefly state how this figure was calculated (see note ii).

2.3 a) Indicate proposed means of discharge - tick as appropriate and show on plan:-
(for 1, 2 & 3 please state dimensions below)

1. Pipe ☐	4. Borehole ☐	7. Sub-Irrigation System ☐
2. Channel ☐	5. Well ☐	8. Combination of 6. & 7. ☐
3. Culvert ☐	6. Soakaway ☐	9. Other *(please specify below)* ☐

b) National Grid Reference(s) of point(s) of discharge (see note iii).

☐☐/☐☐☐☐/☐☐☐☐ *(please indicate on accompanying plans)*

2.4 a) The Agency will normally require adequate provision for the taking of samples of the discharge in a safe and convenient manner at any time. Please indicate the means proposed (see note iv) - tick as appropriate and show on plan:-

At the outlet ☐   At a manhole or sampling chamber ☐

Other *(please specify)* [____]

b) National Grid Reference(s) of sampling point(s). (If different from 2.3 b) above)

☐☐/☐☐☐☐/☐☐☐☐ *(please indicate on accompanying plans)*

c) What flow measurement facilities will be provided (see note v)?
Please give details.

2.5 a) Type of Treatment Plant(s) to be used *(please specify make and model)* - tick as appropriate:-

Septic Tank ☐   Package Sewage Treatment Works ☐   Other ☐

[blank box]

b) Will the treatment process involve the use of any chemicals (eg ferric salts, polyeletrolytes) [Y/N]
   If yes please give details.

[blank box]

2.6 a) On what date do you anticipate the discharge will commence?   [/ /]

b) If you require the consent for a limited time period please give dates;   from: [/ /]

   to: [/ /]

c) If the discharge is not continuous please detail the period/circumstances when it will occur.

[blank box]

2.7 a) Are there any existing consents for discharge from the premises (see note vi)?   [Y/N]
     If yes, please give the reference numbers *(Any further information should be given in section 5.3)*.

[blank box]

b) Has any person had a Prohibition Notice served on them in respect of this site?   [Y/N]
   If yes, please give the reference number.

[blank box]

3   SITE DETAILS

3.1 Please give the name of the relevant Planning Authority.

[blank box]

3.2 Please give details of the premises - tick as appropriate:-

1. Single Dwelling ☐   6. Fish Farm ☐
2. Multiple Dwellings ☐   7. Mineral Workings ☐
3. Industrial Premises ☐   8. Water Services plc STW ☐
4. Vehicle Parking Area ☐   9. Water Supply ☐
5. Commercial Premises *(please specify)* ☐   10. Other *(please specify)* ☐

[blank box]   [blank box]

3.3   Please indicate source of the water supply - tick as appropriate:-

1. Well ☐   5. River *(please give name below)* ☐

2. Borehole ☐   6. Estuary *(please give name below)* ☐

3. Precipitation (eg. rain or snow) ☐   7. Coastal Water *(please give name below)* ☐

4. Mains *(please state water supply company)* ☐

[   ]   [   ]

4   DETAILS OF RECEIVING ENVIRONMENT

4.1   Receiving Medium - tick the category(s) to which the proposed discharge(s) is(are) to be made:-

1. Estuarial Water (tidal river or stream) ☐   5. Into Land ☐

2. River or Stream (non-tidal) ☐   6. Onto Land ☐

3. Canal ☐   7. Directly into Groundwater ☐

4. Lake, Loch or Pond ☐   8. Coastal Water (see note vii) ☐

State name of receiving water if known:

[   ]

4.2   In the case of sub-irrigation systems, soakaways or boreholes:-

(a) Is any part of the system within 5 metres of the boundary of the premises?   [Y/N]

(b) Is any part of the system within 10 metres of a watercourse?   [Y/N]

(c) Is any part of the system within 50 metres of a borehole or spring?   [Y/N]

(d) For wells and boreholes state dimension(s) in metres.   [m]

(e) For sub-irrigation systems, soakaway pits, wells and boreholes, state maximum depth in metres.
[m]

(f) For boreholes, state details of lining in metres:

(i) Depth of lining   [m]

(ii) Depth of perforated lining   [m]

(iii) Depth of unperforated lining   [m]

(g) A percolation test must be carried out in accordance with British Standard BS6297:1983.
Have the results been provided?   [Y/N]

4.3   Is there a foul sewer available to which the discharge(s) could be made (see note viii)?   [Y/N]
If yes, please give the reasons it is not practical to connect to it (eg. distance, flow etc.).

[   ]

5 DETAILS OF APPLICANT AND OTHER INFORMATION

5.1   (See general notes and note ix)

(a)   Full name and postal address of applicant. This should be the person who will become the consent holder should consent be issued.

    *

    *

    *

    *

    *

    *

Post Code:

Daytime Telephone Number:

Company Registration Number (if appropriate):

(b) Agent (if any) - Full name and postal address.

    *

    *

    *

    *

    *

    *

Post Code:

Contact Name and Daytime Telephone Number:

5.2

Please give full name and address to which bills should be sent if different to that given above:

    *

    *

    *

    *

    *

    *

Post Code:

Daytime Telephone Number:

5.3 Are there any other factors to be taken into account? Please continue on a separate sheet if necessary.

DECLARATION

I/We:

1. apply under the Water Resources Act 1991 (as amended by the Environment Act 1995) for consent to discharge, as described in this Application. "This Application" means this page, all the other pages of this form and any attached annexes, the attached plan(s), any other sheets attached, and any other written information supplied to support the application.

2. enclose the required application fee, payable to the Environment Agency (see note x).

3. enclose 3 copies of the plan(s) and location maps with all relevant information clearly marked (see note xi).

4. will pay required advertising costs (see note xii).

5. confirm that I/we* will notify the Environment Agency of any changes in the information in this application which might be material to the continuation of the consent.

6. confirm that the information given in this application and any questions which the Environment Agency may have about it is/will* be true to the best of my/our* knowledge, information and belief and am/are* not aware of any other facts or information which might affect the granting of a consent, or conditions which might be put on it (see note xiii).

7. confirm that I/we* will pay any annual charges due should a consent be granted YES/NO*. If no please indicate who will by completing section 5.2 above (see note xiv).

(* Delete as appropriate)

SIGNED: .... PRINT NAME: ....

ON BEHALF OF:.. DATED: ....

- o O o -

CONFIDENTIALITY

I/we apply for commercial confidentiality and enclose a full written justification (see note xv).

SIGNED: .... DATED: ....

PLEASE RETURN THIS FORM TO THE ADDRESS GIVEN ON THE FRONT PAGE

JWE/TR/MAR96   TR/FMC

WATER RESOURCES ACT 1991
(as amended by the Environment Act 1995)

Notes for Guidance of Applicant for Consent to Discharge

General

Before submission of this form the applicant should ensure that all the information is correct (see note xiii). Liaison with area/district staff is strongly recommended and any doubt about the detailed information required should be discussed with Agency staff before completing the application. Should you wish other matters to be taken into account with the application, additional sheets may be used.

The terms "applicant" and "holder" should be noted. The consent holder is the only person who can claim the benefits of a consent as a protection.

The Agency has four months from the date on which a valid application is received (or such further period as may be agreed upon in writing between the applicant and the Agency) to determine the application, otherwise it is deemed to have been refused by the Agency (this does not affect your rights of appeal). If you have any questions about the form then please contact the officer named below or contact your local Agency office:-

NAME ....

ADDRESS ....

....

....

PHONE ....

Details of Discharges

i)   The Water Resources Act 1991 (as amended by the Environment Act 1995) provides for consent to be granted for sewage effluent, trade effluent or other matter. Note that cooling water, or run-off contaminated as a result of the carrying on of a trade or industrial activity are both trade effluents (eg. run-off from a coal yard, oil storage areas or vehicle loading areas are trade effluents). In these cases Annexe 3 should be completed in addition to the main application form. For all discharges of sewage effluent containing a trade component Annexe 3 should be completed in addition to Annexe 1.

ii)   The maximum quantity should be given in cubic metres per day (please note that 1000 litres is equivalent to 1 cubic metre). The notes below may be of help in calculating the volume:

      a) A per capita volume of 180 litres per head per day will be accepted as the norm, when calculating daily volumes for sewage discharges for consent application purposes. For special cases see table in c) below.

      b) In the absence of accurate population data an estimated population assuming 1 person per bedroom plus 0.5 persons per household will be acceptable.

      c) Deviations from the norm may be accepted in special cases, provided the Agency are satisfied they are specifically justified and adequate evidence is provided. In the case of non-residential properties lower consumption will be generally accepted, as given in the following table.

Property	Per Capita Volume (litres per day)
Hotels	200
Restaurants	25
Campsites	75
Dayschool	50
Boarding school	180
Offices	55
Factories	65
Public Houses	15
Caravans	120
Rest Homes	300
Hospitals	450

(NB 1000 litres is equivalent to one cubic metre)

For combined discharges give figures for each component separately. If infiltration is significant, full details should be provided separately.

iii) If there is more than one point of discharge please provide the extra grid references in section 5.3 (additional information) and for each discharge point/outlet clearly mark the plan with the appropriate identity code e.g. outlet 1,2,3 or A,B,C.

iv) Samples will normally be taken by filling a container at the discharge point where possible. If this is not practicable then a sampling chamber should be provided between the source of the effluent (after any treatment that is to be provided) and the discharge point.

v) The volume of effluent discharged may need to be monitored. Facilities to enable the Agency's Officers to measure the volume must be provided. In some cases there will be a requirement for the discharger to monitor the volume on a regular basis and maintain a log of the readings. Details of the siting and type of flow measurement facilities should be given.

vi) Details should be given of any existing Consent granted under the provisions of the Rivers (Prevention of Pollution) Acts 1951 to 1961; Section 72 of the Water Resources Act 1963; the Lee Conservancy Acts 1868 to 1938; the Port of London Acts 1964 to 1968; Section 34 of the Control of Pollution Act 1974, the Water Act 1989, Environmental Protection Act 1990 and/or the Water Resources Act 1991.

Details of Receiving Environment

vii) For discharges to coastal waters, details of the length of the outfall, distance below low water and dispersion characteristics should be supplied.

viii) Where a foul sewer is available, consent may not be granted unless sufficient evidence is provided to prove connection to the foul sewer is impracticable.

Details of Applicant and Other Information

ix) Please state clearly the status of the applicant (e.g. limited company, partnership, trader, individual). If an agents name is given in Section 5.1(b) it will be assumed they are acting fully on behalf of the applicant and all correspondence will be addressed to them.

If the application is by:

- a **COMPANY** then the registered office address and the Company Registration Number should be given in addition to the full company name (if correspondence should be addressed elsewhere, please indicate clearly);

- a **FIRM** or **PARTNERSHIP** then the full names and addresses of all the relevant partners should be given together with the name the firm trades under and its main addresses;

- a **CLUB** then the full names and addresses of all trustees should be given or the name and address of the person properly authorised to be the consent holder on behalf of the club, in the absence of any trustees.

- a **CHARITY** which is a limited company, please supply the details listed above for clubs; alternatively if the charity is not a limited corporation, the full names and addresses of all trustees should be given.

If approved, a consent will be granted in the name of the applicant. In the case of a company or individual, this is straightforward. In the case of a firm or partnership, club or charity, please consider carefully the names of the trustees which are identified as the applicants. There are special rules concerning subsequent transfer of consents. You will need to advise the agency of any change in trustees in the future.

x) For your guidance the current charges in respect of making an application are set out below. Please note that these may change from time to time and it is advisable to confirm the present sums prior to submitting an application.

(a) for <u>each</u> discharge of sewage effluent of not more than 5m³/day
- £88 *92*

(b) for <u>each</u> discharge of cooling water of not more than 10m³/day
- £88 *92*

(c) for <u>each</u> discharge of <u>uncontaminated</u> surface water
- £88 *92*

(d) in all other cases for <u>each</u> discharge
- £617 *645*

A cheque for the application fee payable to the *Environment Agency* should be enclosed with the application.

xi)   The applicant should attach a site plan (preferably A4 size) showing in detail:

    (a)   the location of the premises. This should be such as to enable a stranger to the area to readily locate the premises. The premises should be clearly indicated. For rainfall dependent discharges, catchment areas should be highlighted.

    (b)   the discharge, sampling points and any other information requested in the application form clearly marked with arrows and labels as necessary.

xii)   Details of the application may need to be published in accordance with the Water Resources Act 1991 (as amended by the Environment Act 1995). In that event, the application will be advertised in a local newspaper and in the London Gazette. The cost of this is payable by the applicant upon demand. In addition to the cost of the advertisement, which will vary depending on local circumstances, an administration charge, not exceeding £50, plus VAT at the standard rate, will be payable.

xiii)   If any person, in furnishing any information or making any application under or for the purposes of any provision of the Act, makes any statement which he knows to be false or misleading in a material particular, he shall be guilty of an offence and liable:-

    (a)   on summary conviction to a fine not exceeding the statutory maximum;
    (b)   on conviction or indictment, to a fine or imprisonment, not exceeding two years, or both.

xiv)   The Agency's costs of dealing with applications are payable by the applicant at the time of submission (see note x). A further annual charge may also be payable from the date of coming into force of any consent issued. This will be invoiced separately after the consent is issued. The enclosed leaflet sets out details of the charging scheme (if no leaflet is enclosed please contact your local Agency office who should be able to provide one). If you have any questions please ask. Details of the local contact are given above.

xv)   The Agency maintains a statutory register, which is available for public inspection, including details of:-

    (a)   applications for consent

    (b)   any consent granted and conditions imposed

    (c)   samples of effluent taken by the Agency

    (d)   information produced by analyses of the samples and the steps taken in consequence of the information

Access to the public register by certain companies may result in unsolicited mail being received. Requirements under the Water Resources Act 1991 (as amended by the Environment Act 1995) mean that the Agency cannot prevent access to the Public Register by such companies.

Any claim for commercial confidentiality will have to be determined by the Agency and could lead to a delay in the determination of the application.

Any request for information to be withheld from the public register <u>must</u> include a full justification for why the information needs to be withheld.

JWE/TR/MAR96   TR/FMC

S E P A

APPLICATION FORM
for
Licence
to
Abstract Water

PLEASE SEND THIS FORM TO:

**The Director,
Scottish Environment Protection Agency,
EAST REGION,
Clearwater House,
Heriot Watt Research Park,
Avenue North,
Riccarton,
EDINBURGH,
EH14 4AP**

**Tel: 0131 449 7296
Fax: 0131 449 7277**

WEST REGION	NORTH REGION	HEAD OFFICE
5 Redwood Crescent	Graesser House	Erskine Court
Peel Park	Fodderty Way	Castle Business Park
East Kilbride	Dingwall Business Park	STIRLING
GLASGOW	DINGWALL	FK9 4TR
G74 5PP	Ross-shire	
	IV15 9XB	
Tel. 01355 574200	Tel. 01349 86021	Tel. 01786 457700
Fax. 01355 574688	Fax. 01349 863987	Fax. 01786 446885

Date received		Validated		Map	Y/N
		Acknowledged		Granted	
Application No.		Fee Paid	Y/N	Refused	

NOTES TO APPLICATION TO ABSTRACT WATER UNDER THE NATURAL HERITAGE (SCOTLAND) ACT 1991

This is an application for a licence, or a variation of a licence, under Section 17 of the Natural Heritage (Scotland) Act 1991 to abstract water for irrigation from inland or ground waters within a control area, as defined in that Act.

Please read the following notes before completing and submitting your form.

1. A licence is not required if you do not intend to abstract water in 2001.

2. The closing date for receipt of applications is 15 September 2000. Your application form, fee and supporting documents must be received by the Scottish Environment Protection Agency (SEPA) by that date.

3. The licence will be valid from 1 January to 31 December 2001.

4. A licence fee of £50 must be enclosed with each application for a licence to abstract. Your application will be incomplete if this is not enclosed.

5. Application for a licence must be made by the occupier (either at the time of application or when the licence comes into force) of the land to be irrigated within the Control Area.

6. After the closing date for receipt of applications, SEPA will publish a notice in a newspaper circulating in the Control Area detailing:-

   i)   any applications they have received
   ii)   where and when such applications can be inspected, and
   iii) the period in which objections should be made.

7. SEPA will keep at its offices in Riccarton a register detailing any application made or licence granted in the Control Area. The register will be available for inspection by any person free of charge at all reasonable hours.

8. Applications for licences may be refused, granted unconditionally or may include conditions such as:-

   i)   means of abstraction
   ii) point of abstraction
   iii) amount of water to be abstracted during any period
   iv) periods during which water may be abstracted

   or any other reasonable conditions which SEPA considers appropriate.

9. SEPA must tell you its decision on the application by 10 November 2000. If SEPA fails to tell you its decision by this date then a licence will be granted unconditionally.

10. If your application is refused SEPA will notify you in writing giving the reasons for refusal.

11. SEPA may consider at any time an application for a licence provided it is satisfied that in all the circumstances, you could not reasonably have met the closing date. If you do apply late, you must advertise your application in a newspaper circulating in the Control Area.

12. If you are granted a licence to abstract water this does not guarantee that the amount of water authorised will in fact be available.

13. If you are not happy with SEPA's decision to grant or refuse your application or with the conditions which are imposed, you can appeal to the Scottish Ministers. You must appeal in writing within 28 days of the day on which you received SEPA's decision and you must send a copy of your written appeal to SEPA.

14. If you do not understand any of these notes, would like more guidance on what is required by the application form or want more information about abstraction or the Control Area, please contact SEPA (East Region) Hydrology Section on 0131 449 7296.

APPLICATION FORM

PLEASE COMPLETE ALL QUESTIONS.

PLEASE TICK THE FOLLOWING:

I have enclosed the fee of £50.

I have enclosed an Ordnance Survey
map to a scale of 1:10,000 (or six
inches to one mile) (see Questions 4 & 8)

1. Name of Applicant

2. Address of Applicant

3. If you have an advisor or agent to
    whom communications on this
    application should be sent, give
    details.

4. Location and National Grid
    Reference of point of abstraction.
    You must provide a map showing
    the abstraction points.

    NGR

5. Name of watercourse, if applicable, from which water will be abstracted.

    [   ]

6. Maximum rate of abstraction.

    [   ] per hour

    [   ] per day

    [   ] per week

7. How will the quantity of water abstracted be measured?

    [   ]

8. Area (ha) of land to be irrigated. You should show this area on the map by shading or marking the boundary.

    [   ]

9. Method of irrigation (eg by stationary pump and raingun).

    [   ]

10. Purpose for which water will be used. If irrigation of crops, state what crops.

    [   ]

11. If water abstracted is to be stored,

    Location:

please give details of location and
volume of storage.

Volume:

12. I am applying for a licence to abstract water for irrigation under the Natural Heritage (Scotland) Act 1991. I declare that to the best of my knowledge the information I have supplied in this application is true.

Your signature ....

Date ....

CONTROL OF POLLUTION ACT 1974 (as amended) APPLICATION FORM FOR CONSENT TO DISCHARGE

Please fill in this form if you want to apply for consent to discharge sewage effluent, trade effluent or any other matter including surface water.

Please return this form to:
The Divisional Manager
Scottish Environment Protection Agency
SEPA WEST
5 Redwood Crescent
Peel Park
EAST KILBRIDE
G74 5PP
Tel. 01355 574 200   Fax. 01355 574688

EAST REGION	NORTH REGION	HEAD OFFICE
Clearwater House	Graesser House	Erskine Court
Heriot Watt Research Park	Fodderty Way	Castle Business Park
Avenue North	Dingwall Business Park	STIRLING
Riccarton	DINGWALL	FK9 4TR
EDINBURGH	Ross-shire	
EH14 4AP	IV15 9XB	
Tel. 0131 449 7296	Tel. 01349 862021	Tel. 01786 457700
Fax. 0131 449 7277	Fax. 01349 863987	Fax. 01786 446885

scottish environment protection agency

Consent application form : swpc1.doc [version 2, June 1997]

1

DECLARATION   *(the declaration must be signed)*

Advertising

Under section 36 of the Control of Pollution Act 1974 (as amended) we have to advertise this application unless the discharge will have no appreciable effect upon the receiving water. The advertisements will appear twice in a local newspaper and once in the Edinburgh Gazette.   You will have to pay for these advertisements even if the application is eventually refused.

If you do not want your application to be advertised, you can apply to the Secretary of State for a "certificate of exemption" (under section 36(2A & 2B). You will only get a certificate if advertising your application could prejudice your commercial interests to an unreasonable degree, or if the release of the information would be prejudicial to the interests of national security.

Please tick one of the following:
I intend to apply to the Secretary of State for a "certificate of exemption" from advertising

Yes		No	

Public Register

Under section 41 of the Control of Pollution Act 1974 (as amended), we have to keep a register of the details of applications to discharge effluent. The public can look at this register and commercial firms selling treatment equipment also use it to find clients.   Under sections 42A and 42B it is possible to gain exclusion from public registers on the basis of commercial confidentiality or in the interests of national security.

Please tick one of the following:
I wish to exclude information submitted with this application from the public register on the grounds of commercial confidentiality

Yes		No	

Note: If you tick "yes", please provide supporting documentation to justify your claim.

I am applying under Section 34 of the Control of Pollution Act 1974 (as amended) for a consent to discharge.   I confirm that the information provided in this form and in any associated documents is correct.   I understand that it is an offence under section 34(5) of the Control of Pollution Act 1974 (as amended) to knowingly or recklessly make any false statement in an application for consent.

Your (or your Agent's) signature	Date

FOR OFFICE USE ONLY

Consent application form : swpc1.doc [version 2, June 1997]

2

BEFORE YOU FILL IN THIS FORM PLEASE READ THE NOTES AT THE BACK

You should fill in this form for all discharges of trade and sewage effluent to controlled waters. If SEPA has issued you with a Prohibition Notice, you should fill in this form for discharges of trade effluent and sewage effluent to land or the discharge of other matter (eg surface water) to controlled waters.

APPLICATION FEES

The charge for a consent application to discharge will be subject to change. You should contact your local SEPA office for information on the current charges.

I have enclosed the fee of   £

IMPORTANT   Please send your payment when you send us your application. If you do not, we can not consider your application. Please make your cheque payable to "Scottish Environment Protection Agency" and write "A/C Payee only" across it.

SECTION A: GENERAL INFORMATION

1. Full address of the property from which you want to discharge effluent. (*If there is no address, please give details which will help us locate the site*).	Address Postcode Daytime telephone No. FAX No.

2. Details of applicant and agent

Your name: Address Postcode Daytime telephone No. FAX No. email address:	Agent's (if any) name: Address Postcode Daytime telephone No. FAX No. email address:

3. What is the National Grid Reference of the site? (*6 or 8 figure*)	N

4. Will the effluent come from:	a new development?		an alteration to an existing development?		an existing development?	

Consent application form : swpc1.doc [version 2, June 1997]

3

5. If the proposal represents an alteration to an existing development, please provide the existing discharge consent reference number.	

6. In which Local Council Area is the site located.	

7. Do you have planning permission for the development (if so, please provide the planning ref. no.)	

8. Describe the discharge (eg treated sewage effluent and/or storm sewage; effluent from a defined trade process, surface water).	

9. Will the discharge be made through: (please tick)	a new outlet?		an alteration to an existing outlet?		an existing outlet?	

10. Where will the outlet discharge to: (please tick)	freshwater -river or loch		freshwater via partial soakaway		land via a soakaway	
	groundwater		coastal waters or estuary		other	

11. What is the name of the receiving water?	

12. What is the national grid reference of the outlet? (6 or 8 figure)	N

13. What material will the outlet be made of? (eg fireclay, plastic, concrete etc)	

14. What will be the internal diameter of the outlet? (in millimetres)	mm

15. What provision will be made for samples to be taken of the effluent discharged? (eg sampling chamber, automatic sampler)	

16. What will the effluent be composed of? (for sewage discharges please provide a description of any significant trade discharges to sewer).	

Note: *Does the untreated effluent contain any compound listed in the Annex to this form? If so, please give the mean annual concentration of each substance in the influent flow and the maximum concentration and mean annual concentration in the outflow. You should include information on the daily, weekly and/or seasonal patterns, if these are likely to be significant.*

Consent application form : swpc1.doc [version 2, June 1997]

4

SECTION B SEWAGE EFFLUENT

Note: You should fill in form SWPC2 for discharges of sewage from up to and including four houses or from a population equivalent of less than 15.

1. What population equivalent(PE) load will the sewer serve?(*both current PE and projected design PE*)	

Note: For small developments a map should be provided which defines the catchment area of the sewer and the drainage layout. For large municipal drainage systems access to the drainage plans should already be available.

2. What is the anticipated flow of domestic sewage? *(in cubic metres per day)*	m³/d

Note: Please explain how the flows have been derived. In particular you should specify the details of any flow monitoring programmes.

3. What is the anticipated flow of trade effluent? *(in cubic metres per day)*	m³/d

Note: Please explain how the flows have been derived. In particular you should specify the details of any flow monitoring programmes.

4. What is the average infiltration rate? *(in cubic metres per day)*	m³/d

Note: Please explain how the flows have been derived. In particular you should specify the details of any flow monitoring programmes carried out to estimate the infiltration rate.   Details of seasonal variations in infiltration flow should be provided if possible.

5. What is the current and design dry weather flow? *(in cubic metres per day)*	Current	m³/d
	Design	m³/d

Note: Please explain how the flows have been derived.

Consent application form : swpc1.doc [version 2, June 1997]

5

Combined sewer overflows

6. At what rate of flow will the overflow start operating?
(litres per second and as a multiple of DWF)

l/s   DWF

Note: Please explain the choice of overflow setting

7. What will the maximum rate of discharge be?
(litres per second and as a multiple of DWF)

l/s   DWF

8. What treatment will be provided?

Note: Please enclose supporting documentation covering detailed plans and design criteria

9. What storage volume in excess of DWF will be provided within the sewerage system which will delay the operation of the overflow
(in cubic metres)

m³

10. What is the predicted spill frequency per year?
(number and duration)

Note: Please provide an explanation of how the predicted spill frequency of the overflow was derived.

Storm tanks

11. What storm tank volume will be available?
(in cubic metres)

m³

12. How will the return of storm tank contents be achieved?
(describe whether manual/automatic return, and pump rates)

Consent application form : swpc1.doc [version 2, June 1997]

6

Emergency overflows

13. Describe the pump rates

14. What sort of warning system will you use to identify pump failure/operation of overflow?
    (eg alarms, telemetry connections)

15. How will you deal with power failures?

16. What storage capacity will be provided which will delay the operation of the overflow?*(in cubic metres)*

m^3

Sewage treatment works

17. What will be the mean daily flow of effluent?
    (in cubic metres per day)

m^3/d

Note: Please explain how the flows provided have been derived. In particular you should specify the details of any flow monitoring programmes.

18. What will be the maximum flow to full treatment?
    (in litres per second and as a multiple of DWF)

l/s   DWF

19. How will the sewage be treated before it is discharged?

Note: Please enclose supporting documents which should include detailed plans, design criteria, and process description

20. How will mechanical failures of the treatment facilities be detected? *(eg telemetry, alarms)*

SECTION C: TRADE EFFLUENT

1. Please describe the type of process you plan to carry out on the site.

2. List bulk environmentally hazardous chemicals and wastes held on site and explain how these will be prevented from posing a threat to surface or groundwater.

3. What will be the mean and maximum daily volume of treated effluent discharged? *(in cubic metres per day)*	Mean	m^3/d
	Maximum	m^3/d

Note: *You should include information on the weekly and/or seasonal patterns, if these are likely to be significant.*

4. Please provide the maximum rate of flow of the treated effluent *in litres per second)*		l/s

5. Please provide the mean and expected temperature range of the discharge. *(in degrees centigrade)*	Mean:	°C
	Range:	°C

Consent application form : swpc1.doc [version 2, June 1997]

8

6. How will the effluent be treated before it is discharged?

Note: Please enclose supporting documents which should include detailed plans, design criteria, and treatment process description

7. How will mechanical failures of the treatment facilities be detected? *(eg telemetry, alarms)*

8. If sewage is included in this discharge, how many people will the system serve?

9. What impermeable surface area will drain rainfall to the treatment system? *(in square metres)* m^2

Note: Uncontaminated surface water should be excluded from the effluent treatment plant where possible.

10. How will any remaining surface water be treated?

Note: If you will be making a separate discharge of surface water, you should discuss with SEPA whether it will be necessary to fill in Section D of this form

Consent application form : swpc1.doc [version 2, June 1997]

9

SECTION D: SURFACE WATER AND ANY OTHER MATTER

Note: Please fill in this section if you have been issued with a Prohibition Notice which necessitates a consent application.   A Prohibition Notice may not be issued so long as SEPA is satisfied that adequate treatment provision has been provided.   For further information see: "A guide to surface water best management practices" published by SEPA.

Surface water

1. Please describe the area drained *(eg a 50 house development)*

Note: *Plans should be provided showing: (1) the site location; (2) the area draining to the discharge - detailing the drainage system proposed including pipes and open channels, as well as existing natural drainage features; (3) planned development features including roads, parking areas and buildings.*

2. Will there be any high pollution risk areas?
   (This refers to areas such as re-fuelling/ wash bays or unloading areas)

Note: *Please provide a plan of the relevant area and a description of the preventative measures taken (eg oil interceptor, diversion to foul sewer, bunding)*

3. What will be the total impervious area which will drain rainfall to the outfall? *(in square metres and as a proportion of the total drainage area)*

	m^2
	%

4. What provision will be made to direct rainfall towards drainage into land?

Note: *This refers to the use of permeable surfaces, infiltration trenches, infiltration basins etc which limit the direct access of rainfall to surface water drains. Please provide drawings of the structure used and documentation covering the design.*

5. What in-site treatment will be provided?

Note: *This refers to structures such as subsurface reservoirs, swales, filtration drains and ponds used within the surface water drains. Please provide drawings of the structure used and documentation covering the design.*

6. If infiltration systems are to be installed please provide information on soil type and porosity.

7. What end-of-pipe treatment will be provided?

Note: This refers to structures such as ponds and wetlands used where other within-site treatment systems have not been installed or do not provide full protection. Please provide drawings of the structure used and documentation covering the design.

Other matter

8. Please describe the method of treatment.

SECTION E: DISCHARGING EFFLUENT TO A SOAKAWAY, ONTO LAND OR DIRECTLY UNDERGROUND

Note: You must fill in this section for any discharges of effluent direct to ground water. You should also fill in this section if you will be discharging trade and sewage effluent to land and SEPA has issued you with a Prohibition Notice, necessitating a consent application.

1. Are there any wells or water abstraction points within 100 metres of the discharge point?	

Note: If there are any potentially affected abstraction points, please provide a map with their location clearly marked relative to the discharge point.

Discharging directly underground

2. What sort of strata will the effluent be discharged into? *(eg carboniferous limestone, coal measures)*

Note: Please enclose a map showing the location of the site. SEPA may require a hydro-geological survey to assess the risks to ground water.

Discharging to a soakaway

3. Please provide results of percolation tests carried out at the site.

Note: A certificate should be provided and signed by an independent relevant professional (eg architect, soil engineer or building control officer) presenting the percolation results and calculations. The certificate should confirm that the test was carried out according to BS 6297. 1983

4. Please provide details of the soakaway construction.

Note: A certificate should be provided and signed by a independent relevant professional (eg architect, soil engineer, or building control officer) describing the design and construction of the soakaway. The certificate should confirm that the soakaway conforms with BS 6297 1983 or provide justification for any difference.

Discharging onto land

5. Please give details of the land used for disposal. This should include soil type and underlying geology.

Note: Please enclose a map showing the location of the site. SEPA may require a hydro-geological survey to assess the risks to ground and surface water. You should also provide details of application rates and control systems.

Consent application form : swpc1.doc [version 2, June 1997]

13

PLEASE READ THESE NOTES BEFORE YOU FILL THIS FORM IN.

You should fill in this form for all discharges of trade and sewage effluent to controlled waters. If SEPA has issued you with a Prohibition Notice, you should fill in this form for discharges of trade effluent and sewage effluent to land or the discharge of other matter (eg surface water) to controlled waters. The application form and supporting details must be submitted in duplicate.

Please note that you should not fill in this form for discharges of sewage from small developments of up to four houses or from a population equivalent of less than 15 (use form SWPC2). Similarly you should fill in form SWPC7 if you wish to discharge effluent from a fish farm.

This form is designed to provide SEPA with the information required to assess an application for discharge consent. Please fill in the sections of the form according to the guidance provided in the table below. You should then sign the form and enclose the application fee.

Type of Effluent	Answer Sections	Pages
Fish farms	(use form SWPC 7)	
Sewage effluent from less than 4 houses or less than 15 people	(use form SWPC 2)	
Sewage effluent	A , B (& E if appropriate)	3, 4, 5, 6, 7 (12 & 13)
Trade effluent	A , C (& E if appropriate)	3, 4, 8, 9 (12 & 13)
Surface water or any other matter	A , D (& E if appropriate)	3, 4, 10, 11 (12 & 13)

Supporting information
Under section 34(1) of the Control of Pollution Act 1974 (as amended) we may require such information as may reasonably be needed to assess an application for consent to discharge. In addition to enclosing a completed application form, some supporting documentation is required. You should discuss detailed requirements with the local SEPA office. However, you should include:

1. A map showing the location of the site.
2. A plan showing the layout of the drainage system showing positions of the buildings, treatment plant, sampling chamber, soakaway and/or outlet. The location of any nearby watercourses or drains should also be shown.
3. Details of the design and expected performance of any effluent treatment plants which already exist or which will be built or altered.
4. The design of the outlet and sampling chamber.
5. Details of any other outlet from the same site or drainage system.

Refusal of consent application
You can assume that your application has been refused if:
- we notify you of a decision to refuse the application; or
- we do not give you a decision within four months of receiving it (or any other deadline you agree to in writing).

If we refuse your application or impose conditions which you consider unreasonable, you can appeal to the Secretary of State under section 39 of the Control of Pollution Act 1974 (as amended). The detailed procedure for doing this is set out in Regulation 7 of the Control of Pollution (Consents for Discharges)(Secretary of State Functions) Regulations 1984 (SI 1984 No 865). This generally requires notice of appeal, with a statement of the grounds, to be given in writing to the Secretary of State. You must send this notice to the Secretary of State within three months of the refusal date or the issue of the consent.

Appeals should be sent to: The Secretary of State for Scotland, Determinations Unit, Environmental Affairs Groups, 14 Victoria Quay, Edinburgh, EH6 6QQ.

Consent application form : swpc1.doc [version 2, June 1997]

14

DEFINITIONS

Biochemical Oxygen Demand (BOD)
A measure of biodegradable organic pollution in water .

BOD load
The total amount of biodegradable organic pollution in water. To work out the BOD load, multiply the BOD by the volume of water.

Discharge
Dispose of liquid waste.

Dry weather flow(DWF)
Normally the flow in a sewer or drain following a period of at least 7 days without rain.

Effluent
A liquid, normally sewage or trade waste, flowing out of a waste treatment system.

Gross solids
Large organic matter and floating solids, such as paper, faeces, rags, pieces of wood or plastic.

Outlet/outfall
A pipe or channel at the point where the effluent discharges into controlled waters.

Population equivalent
The term used to express the BOD load of waste water. To work out the population equivalent, multiply the daily flow of the discharge (in m^3) by the average BOD (in mg/l) and divide by 60. (60g is the average BOD load for one person in a day.)

Sampling Chamber
A manhole or other chamber designed to allow the collection of a representative sample of the effluent before it is discharged from the outlet (SEPA can provide details of an acceptable design).

Soakaway
An underground area, either natural or man-made, into which effluent finally flows and soaks away.

Soil porosity
The ability of soil to soak up or drain away liquids.

Tidal waters
All waters, including estuaries of rivers, which are affected by the tide. The Secretary of State has officially defined tidal waters for the purpose of your application, and we have maps showing the defined areas.

Controlled waters
Surface water such as rivers and lochs; groundwater and water in non-municipal drains; estuaries and coastal waters up to 3 miles from the coast.
Standing waters which does not drain into controlled waters is excluded.

Water abstraction point
A place on a river, a well or spring where water is removed for drinking water supplies, industrial production processes or other purposes.

Consent application form : swpc1.doc [version 2, June 1997]

15

ANNEX

The following substances are listed in EC Directives or the UK Red List and are considered to be dangerous if they are discharged into water.

1 Metals and their compounds, and substances which are similar to metals
Antimony
Arsenic
Barium
Beryllium
Boron
Cadmium
Chromium
Cobalt
Copper
Lead
Mercury
Molybdenum
Nickel
Selenium
Silver
Tellurium
Thallium
Tin
Titanium
Uranium
Vanadium
Zinc

2 Organohalogen pesticides
Aldrin
DDT
1,2 - dichloroethane
Dieldrin
Endosulfan
Endrin
Gamma - hexachlorocyclohexane
Hexachlorobenzene
Pentachlorophenol
Polychlorinated biphenyls
Trichlorobenzene

Any other organohalogen compounds and substances which may form these compounds

3 Organophosphorus or organonitrogen pesticides
Azinphos - methyl
Dichlorvos
Fenitrothion
Malathion
Trifluralin
Any other organophosphorus compounds

4 Organotin compounds
Tributyltin compounds
Triphenyltin compounds
Any other organotin compounds

5 Triazine herbicides
Atrazine
Simazine

6 Substances which can cause cancer, mutations or other defects in or through the aquatic environment.

7 Mineral oils and hydrocarbons.

8 Cyanides.

9 Any other biocides or their derivatives.

10 Substances which can affect the taste or smell of groundwater, and compounds which cause these substances to form in groundwater, making it unfit to drink.

11 Poisonous or long-lasting organic compounds of silicon, and substances which cause these compounds to form in water. This does not include compounds which do not harm the environment, or which quickly become harmless when placed in water.

12 Inorganic compounds of phosphorus and elemental phosphorus.

13 Fluorides.

14 Ammonia and nitrites.

Consent application form : swpc1.doc [version 2, June 1997]

16